Issued under the authority of th...

Manual of Firemanship

A survey of the science of fire-fighting

Book 8
Building construction and structural fire protection

London
Her Majesty's Stationery Office

The previous publishing history of
this volume is shown on pages 181/3.

ISBN 0 11 340588 X

Preface

The idea that buildings should offer some resistance to the destructive effects of fire has its origin in the far distant past of most developed countries; it dates from perhaps the 13th century in England. This was probably one of the earliest measures of social protection and it is likely originally to have been intended not so much for the protection of life as of property. When buildings were of a crude and simple kind they were seldom more than two storeys in height; people would be unlikely to have serious difficulty in escaping from a fire in such a building. On the other hand, these buildings were often huddled close together, perhaps within a fortified wall (a form of social protection with a different purpose), and a fire starting among them must often have destroyed them all and rendered a whole township homeless. The possibilities of incendiarism as an act of war were often exploited in the Middle Ages, and perhaps the incorporation of fire resistance into buildings was a primeval measure of 'civil defence'.

As time went on, urban development would give rise to taller and more extensive buildings, whose contents would be of increasing commercial value, and these would offer an increasing risk to life at the same time. Particularly in buildings used for the assembly of large numbers of people, this risk led, very gradually, to the incorporation of design features to facilitate escape. It has begun to be realised only in comparatively recent times that these two forms of protection – resistance to the effects of fire and provision for escape – are complementary to each other: the inherent resistance of a building to the development of a fire will automatically afford some prospect of improved safety for the building's occupants as well as to its contents and, conversely, the provision of adequate means of escape is scarcely practicable in a building which permits the unrestrained growth of a fire occurring within it.

Hence, in modern times, we have an elaborate system of building control designed to ensure, in the public interest, that buildings are so constructed as to retard the spread of fire both within them and between them; a system of insurance rules designed to achieve a similar effect directed to the protection of the contents of buildings; and a sophisticated set of rules and techniques designed to ensure the safe evacuation of occupants. The practical features of the building which are involved in all these three – walls, doors, floors, passages, corridors, columns, beams – are, broadly speaking, the same: it is in their nature, arrangement and relationship that the subtle variations occur which urge the balance of effort in one or other of the three directions referred to.

The roles of the fire brigade – fire fighting, rescue and advice on fire prevention – were developed late in the process of evolution outlined above: fire brigades began as an aid to insurance in the 18th century and the first municipal brigade originated in the second half of the 19th century. Mobile fire escapes, independently of fire brigades, came into tentative use at about the same time, and fire 'cover' – i.e. provision for dealing with fires in a general sense – became a widespread local authority responsibility in 1938. To give advice about fire prevention, again in a wide sense, became a duty of fire authorities in 1947. Since the middle of the present century, there has been a growing tendency to regard fire fighting and especially rescue not as the main protection against fire as an Act of God – as was once the case – but as emergency measures brought in to prevent or counteract a failure on the part of a building or the organisation within it.

Reference was made earlier to the idea that safety from fire spread within a building was obtainable by the correct choice and arrangement of the various features of the building such as walls, floors, beams and columns. While this is effectively true, it is also true that the present century has seen great developments in the fire protection of buildings by another means – sometimes alternative, sometimes complementary to building design and construction. This other means comprises the large number of systems available for installation in buildings and designed to extinguish fires automatically, or to detect them and sound an alarm, or to open vents for smoke and heat, or to produce other effects which will assist in preventing a building from being overrun by a fire, generally as a supplement to the protective features in the design of the building itself.

This *Manual*, Book 8 in the new format series, describes buildings, elements of building construction and the materials used in building, especially from the point of view of their behaviour in fire and the techniques available to the designer for making buildings safer from fire. It does not deal with means of escape as such, though in so far as means of escape relies upon elements of building construction, many of its basic components are described, though only incidentally. A description of fire protection systems will be found in the *Manual*, Book 9.

Home Office
November 1974

Metrication

List of SI units for use in the fire service.

Quantity and basic or derived SI unit and symbol	Approved unit of measurement	Conversion factor
Length metre (m)	kilometre (km) metre (m) millimetre (mm)	1 mile = 1·609 km 1 yard = 0·914 m 1 foot = 0·305 m 1 inch = 25·4 mm
Area square metre (m²)	square kilometre (km²) square metre (m²) square millimetre (mm²)	1 mile² = 2·590 km² 1 yard² = 0·836 m² 1 foot² = 0·093 m² 1 inch = 645·2 mm²
Volume cubic metre (m³)	cubic metre (m³) litre (l) (10^{-3}m³)	1 cubic foot = 0·028 m³ 1 gallon = 4·546 litre
Volume, flow cubic metre per second (m³/s)	cubic metre per second (m³/s) litre per minute (l/min = 10^{-3} m³/min)	1 foot³/s = 0·028 m³/s 1 gall/min = 4·546 l/min
Mass kilogram (kg)	kilogram (kg) tonne (t) = (10^3 kg)	1 lb = 0.454 kg 1 ton = 1·016 t
Velocity metre per second (m/s)	metre/second (m/s) International knot (kn) kilometre/hour (km/h)	1 foot/second = 0·305 m/s 1 UK knot = 1·853 km/h 1 Int. knot = 1·852 km/h 1 mile/hour = 1·61 km/h
Acceleration metre per second² (m/s²)	metre/second² (m/s²)	1 foot/second² = 0·305 m/s² 'g' = 9·81 m/s²

Quantity and basic or derived SI unit and symbol	Approved unit of measurement	Conversion factor
Force newton (N)	kilonewton (kN) newton (N)	1 ton force$=$9·964 kN 1 lb force$=$4·448 N
Energy, work joule (J) ($=1$ Nm)	joule (J) kilojoule (kJ) kilowatt-hour (kWh)	1 British thermal unit $=$1·055 kJ 1 foot lb force$=$1·356 J
Power watt (W) ($=1$ J/s$=1$ Nm/s)	kilowatt (kW) watt (W)/	1 horsepower$=$0·746 kW 1 foot lb force/second$=$ 1·356 W
Pressure newton/metre^2 (N/m^2) $=1$ pascal (Pa)	bar$=10^5$ N/m^2 millibar (mbar) ($=10^2$ N/m^2) metrehead	1 atmosphere$=$ 101·325 kN/m$^2=$ 1·013 bar 1 lb force/in$^2=$ 6894·76 N/m$^2=$0·069 bar 1 inch Hg$=$33·86 mbar 1 metrehead$=$0·0981 bar 1 foot head$=$0·305 metrehead
Heat, quantity of heat joule (J)	joule (J) kilojoule (kJ)	1 British thermal unit $=$1·055 kJ
Heat flow rate watt (W)	watt (W) kilowatt (kW)	1 British thermal unit/ hour$=$0·293 W 1 British thermal unit/ second$=$1·055 kW
Specific energy, calorific value, specific latent heat joule/kilogram (J/kg) joule/m^3 (J/m^3)	kilojoule/kilogram (kJ/kg) kilojoule/m^3 (kJ/m^3) megajoule/m^3 (MJ/m^3)	1 British thermal unit/ lb$=$2·326 kJ/kg 1 British thermal unit/ft$^3=$37·26 kJ/m^3
Temperature degree Celsius (°C)	degree Celsius (°C)	1 degree centigrade$=$ 1 degree Celsius

Contents

Part 1
Building materials

Chapter 1 The character and use of building materials

Chapter 2 Fire testing of materials

Part 2
Elements of structure

Chapter 3 General notes on elements of structure

Chapter 4 True elements of structure

Chapter 5 Other elements of structure

Part 3
Building design

Chapter 10 Examples of buildings

Chapter 11 Services in buildings

Chapter 12 Access for fire appliances to buildings

List of plates

1 An example of the spalling of limestone when subjected to heat and subsequently to cooling by a jet.

2 An example of spalling of concrete of the surface material. Note the protection of the steelwork by the asbestos insulation board remaining intact.
Photo: TAC Construction Materials Ltd

3 The severe effect of heat on unprotected steelwork.

4 The result of expansion of unprotected universal steel sections inside a building causing displacement of the brickwork.

5 The effect of a severe fire on unprotected cast iron columns and universal steel sections.

6 The insulating material filling in a void in a building.

7 Fire propagation test apparatus showing the specimen holder and the calibration board in place. The gas burner can be seen in the apparatus near the bottom with the electric heaters above.
Photo: Building Research Establishment, Fire Research Station

8 The apparatus used for a large-scale surface spread of flame test.
Photo: Building Research Establishment, Fire Research Station

9 One method of construction of a unit of prestressed concrete. Note the ends of the high tensile tendons which appear as black dots.
Photo: Bison Concrete Ltd

10 The manner in which a wattle-and-daub wall was constructed.

11 Prestressed concrete planks.
Photo: Bison Concrete Ltd

12 A prestressed concrete plank floor; also shown is the channelling into which prestressed concrete planks are positioned.
Photo: Bison Concrete Ltd

13 A view of the space between queen posts of a queen post truss utilised as a storage area.
Photo: London Fire Brigade

14   A prime example of cast iron roof trusses and cast iron columns. Note the north light roofing upper right.

15   A typical simple batten and slate roof construction showing the burnt roof timbers having allowed the slates to slide and provide ventilation.
Photo: London Fire Brigade

16   A 17th-century roof structure showing some remaining tile battens and fallen tiles as a result of fire.
Photo: London Fire Brigade

17   Extensive roof collapse of a corrugated iron roof when involved in fire.
Photo: London Fire Brigade

18   A good example of the ability of a closed door to resist the spread of fire. The manner in which hot gases rise is excellently shown by the unaffected lower portions of the woodwork.

19   The effect of heat on wired glass. Note how the window has remained intact and delayed the venting of the fire.

20   An example of lift slab construction.
Photo: British Lift Slab Ltd

21   A lift slab construction showing the storey floor slabs being raised by jacks and parked.
Photo: British Lift Slab Ltd

22   A Portal frame type of construction showing the concrete columns rigidly connected to the structural roof members.
Photo: Bell and Webster Ltd

23   An older type of hotel showing utilisation of roof voids.
Photo: Trust Houses Forte Ltd

24   A modern hotel of framed construction.
Photo: Trust Houses Forte Ltd

25   An older type of hospital building. Note the differing levels at the rear which could promote access difficulties.

26   A modern multi-storey hospital building showing the integrated fire escape on the right.

27   A range of projecting shops. Note the lantern lights in the roof of each shop and that the party walls are carried through the roofs.

28   The traditional church building of solid construction.

29   The interior of a traditional church showing the large open spaces, timber close-boarded roof and timber pews.

30   A modern church exterior used for multi purposes.

31   The interior of a modern church building which shows one of the multi-purpose uses. In this case a play school.

32 An exterior view of a high bay warehouse showing the extent and size of this modern storage facility.
Photo: Shepherd Building Group Ltd

33 An example of a town centre development.
Photo: Bedfordshire County Fire Service

34 An air-supported structure showing the air-lock principle to facilitate easy access against the difference of pressures.
Photo: Gotthard Air Structures (UK) Ltd

35 A multi-storey car park showing the open sides allowing heat and smoke to escape in case of fire.
Photo: London Fire Brigade

36 An interior view of a multi-storey car park.
Photo: London Fire Brigade

37 A typical installation of air recirculating units providing dust extraction for a panel production line in a kitchen furniture factory. Note in this photograph the modular nature of the system reduces the propagation of fire as compared with systems employing large centralised collectors.
Photo: Dust Control Engineering Ltd

38 A conventional cyclone dust separator with a two-way discharge. One feeds a rotary table silo which in turn delivers wood waste to the wood fired air heater automatically and combustion controlled by thermocouples. The other outlet will allow wooden chips to be diverted to an overflow should the silo become full, automatically controlled by a silo level switch. Reduced handling and uncontrolled storage lessens the fire risk.
Photo: Dust Control Engineering Ltd

Part 1
Building materials

The fireman requires to have a thorough and intimate knowledge of building materials for purposes of his professional work. His interest in them is, in fact, twofold: firstly, their character may have a profound effect on the safety of a building's occupants and contents by affecting the manner and rate of fire development in the building. Materials are primarily chosen in building construction because of the advantageous properties they possess in terms of the building itself, its economical construction, its endurance, its use. However, certain standards of behaviour in fire are required of most buildings for the reasons outlined in the preface to this volume, and the choice of materials plays a considerable part in meeting these standards. The fireman must therefore be familiar with the properties of all materials in so far as they contribute to fire safety or danger in a building when incorporated into its structure.

Secondly, the properties of building materials can have marked effects on the difficulties and dangers encountered by the firemen engaged in fighting a fire. These effects are almost a science in themselves: some materials weaken in heat, some disintegrate in fire, some give off poisonous smoke or fumes, some fail without warning when water jets are applied to them in the presence of a high temperature. These and many other characteristics may produce grave risks to life and limb for the fireman in the course of his work, and his safety will depend on a knowledge of them and his ability to detect some signs of dangerous developments. Both of these aspects of building materials are studied in Part 1. The materials used in buildings are listed and described; the system of fire tests at present used in this country for classifying materials according to the properties they show under fire conditions is also described. This system, elaborate and difficult to grasp as it is, is nevertheless imperfect and in constant need of review and development: it is indeed far from complete at the time of publication of this *Manual*. Considerable research effort has been and continues to be invested in the field of fire testing over the last twenty years or so, both in the United Kingdom and in most other developed countries.

Some explanation is due, perhaps, at this point of why the fire testing of materials presents such difficulties and why the system, complex and sophisticated though it is, is still under intensive study. (It should be mentioned at this point that these remarks apply also to the contents of Part 2, which deals with elements of structure.

1

These also come within the field of fire testing and present some, though not as many, of the same kind of difficulties as do building materials themselves.)

The difficulty of assessing the behaviour of materials in a fire situation is that there are so many fire situations. By this is meant not the comparatively simple idea that fire can take place in so many different situations; this should not be a serious difficulty, since a good fire test should indicate, in theory at least, the behaviour of a material in any environmental situation. The difficulty is more complex than this; it is that a material may become involved in fire at various different stages in the development of the fire itself, and the effect of the material's qualities will be different according to what stage has been reached. This makes it necessary to anticipate, in the case of any given material, the kind of fire situation in which it is most likely to be involved, and to test its qualities in this situation. Simultaneously, however, there will be a need to bear in mind alternative possibilities in the origin or behaviour of the fire and ensure that the material will not offer undue risk in these situations either.

A simple example of test is the common sheet of board which might be used for constituting a ceiling. If a small ignition source (a cigarette end perhaps) should find its way on to the upper surface, the board should not be capable of igniting unduly readily; but if the upper surface is not in a void but is pressed against an upper layer, quite different considerations apply. In this case, it is the lower surface of the board which is important, but the nature of the igniting agent cannot be the same in these circumstances. Again, if the board is ignited at its edge, it should not permit flame to spread across its surface with unacceptable speed, but the rate at which this does occur will be greatly affected by whether a fire is in progress in the space beneath the ceiling or not. In both these examples, the situation of the board is the same, but the fire situation is not.

The purpose of a fire testing procedure is to determine the qualities possessed by the material in relation to the wide variety of possible ignition and other effects. There are many other judgements which may have to be made before it is possible to decide what event or events the board being tested is to withstand: it will be seen that this produces a fluid position which offers great problems. Moreover these problems have been greatly accentuated of recent years by yet another development: the increasing use of new building materials – mostly plastics – which have quite different physical properties from most traditional ones. This has meant that the series of fire tests developed under the general heading of British Standard 476 over the years is now having to be used on materials which behave in ways not anticipated when the tests were devised. To illustrate this, one can revert to the example quoted of the board used as a ceiling. If this were made of a material which melted at a lower temperature than that at which it would ignite, the test, as it stood, might well prove unsuitable for that material.

On top of this, it has to be remembered that fire itself is a pheno-menon which, although older than civilisation, is only now revealing the full secrets of its nature under intensive examination. The Fire Research Station is continuously active in fundamental studies of fire itself, including the structure of flames, the effects of ventilation on fire development and the smoke production from burning materials. It is evident that the fire testing of materials – and indeed of elements of structure dealt with in Part 2 – is a developing tech-nique which, when we try to understand and master it, changes almost before we have had time to do so.

One other important aspect of fire testing should be appreciated by the student; the difference between what one may call quality control testing and what is known as environmental testing. This is of great importance, but its effects are not always appreciated. If, for instance, one is interested in the behaviour in fire of textile materials, it is possible to estimate their ignitability and rapidity of burning by simply hanging up a strip of material and igniting the bottom edge. This is quite effective for distinguishing between one material and another and is done for all sorts of purposes: it is quite often the basis for *ad hoc* judgements of a material's suitability for a given purpose. However, a moment's reflection will indicate that if one applied such a test to a piece of material to be used as a decorative wall covering fixed with an adhesive, the *ad hoc* test might well reveal nothing useful whatsoever. Moreover, there are variations of this situation where the *ad hoc* test might be misleading and possibly even dangerous. Sample testing of this 'quality control' kind has its uses, of course, and is indispensable to manufacturers for their own purposes; however, experience has shown that for purposes of determining levels of safe performance in fire, the only form of test on which reliance can be placed is the environmental type of test which examines and classifies materials in situations which corres-pond fairly closely with those in which they will actually be used. The tests in BS 476 are all more or less of an environmental type.

Finally, the reader should not, when faced with a study of the fire properties of materials, come to the false conclusion that fire testing is something to do with an effort to provide non-combustible build-ings, or, least of all, so called 'fire-proof' ones, the latter being an unacceptable term in any case. The selection of building materials for fire safety is always made against the background that it is primarily the contents of buildings that give rise to danger from fire. Non-combustibility of materials is only one of a series of environ-mental fire tests; the system that we have of regulating the choice of materials is designed to control the level of fire risk according to the situation and probable course of a fire's development. It never could hope to abolish the risk or to prevent the fire, and this is not its intention.

Chapter 1
The character and use of building materials

This first chapter is based on a comprehensive list of the materials in general use for the construction of buildings and, to some extent, for their contents. It indicates the uses of these materials and describes their properties insofar as they concern the fireman; these include, where appropriate, their ignitability, fire propagation and/or flame spread characteristics, their behaviour when involved in fire and something of the dangers, if any, that they can offer in the course of fire-fighting operations. It is impracticable, however, to provide details of this kind to cover every possible situation in which a material might be used and every form or combination of forms in which it may appear; the reader is recommended to absorb the details given in this list and extend this to particular cases or situations with the aid of his knowledge of physical principles, such as the properties of matter and the effects of heat.

One point of importance in the fire testing of materials deserves mention at this introductory stage and will be referred to frequently in the text. This is the difference between materials which possess their fire qualities inherently and those whose qualities are added to them at some stage. By 'inherently' is meant that the quality or qualities reside in the physical and chemical composition of the material itself, so that the material will always possess them while it continues to be that material. On the other hand, various forms of treatment are available for different materials which will improve their fire qualities: sometimes this involves surface application, sometimes impregnation. In the case of some plastics materials particularly, there are techniques of adding substances at some stage in manufacture; one might think that this would produce 'inherent' qualities in the finished material, but this is not necessarily so. Any process which might result in an uneven distribution of the additive through the material must be regarded with some reserve.

It is common to find that regulating or purchasing authorities tend to distinguish between materials with an inherent quality and those with an added or applied quality in favour of the former. This is due to various factors, the most important of which is uncertainty as to whether the quality is permanent after it has been added and, if not, whether it will last the life of the material in the given situation.

1 Timber

Although there exist examples of timber-framed houses dating back to Tudor times it would be fair to say that the vast majority of houses constructed in timber in this country have been built since 1964–65. Because this form of construction enables a wide range of claddings to be used (e.g. brick outer skins, tile hanging or cement rendering on metal laths), in addition to timber – which itself can be fixed to otherwise traditional brick houses – it is not always immediately obvious whether or not a house is timber framed. The period mentioned began with the introduction, for the first time, of national building regulations. These, together with accumulated knowledge from other countries having a long and continuing history of timber dwellings, have resulted in standards of construction being adopted in Britain which make the modern timber-framed house once completed, with its fire protective linings, as safe as the more traditional forms.

Apart from agricultural buildings, early industrial premises and some community buildings, timber framing has not, to date, been widely used for buildings other than homes. However, for centuries, timber has commonly been used structurally for floors, roofs, beams and columns, internal partitioning and staircases, in addition to doors, window frames and trims within otherwise brick or stone buildings; these elements and other uses will be considered later. Unlike brick or blockwork walls, which combine strength with weather resistance, timber walls consist of a structural framework with separately applied finishes: externally to keep out the weather and internally for appearance and fire protection.

It is an inescapable fact that timber burns. It has been established that the burning, or charring, rate is predictable and varies only slightly with species of timber, and not on the severity of the fire. Usually (but not always), the higher the density of timber, the greater the *resistance* to charring. Due to its high thermal insulation properties (poor conduction) the timber behind the charring plane is little affected and, as a consequence, is able to perform structurally as designed; albeit to a reduced amount determined by the residual or unaffected cross-section. This knowledge, coupled with the fact that all load-bearing elements of construction are designed with safety factors enabling them to support loads two or more times those actually involved means that there always exists a time factor of safety in timber buildings – irrespective of the additional protection afforded by the linings usually incorporated. These linings often provide the bulk of the fire resistance and may protect the timber frame for an hour or more. A very simple timber-joisted floor with a ceiling of 12·5 mm plasterboard plus a facing of 5 mm thickness of gypsum plaster will provide a minimum half-hour fire resistance. One hour for both flame penetration and resistance to collapse and insulation is the usual minimum requirement for floors between flats of three or more storeys; this is achieved without difficulty by properly designed timber-joisted floors incorporating 32 mm plasterboard ceilings. Loadbearing timber-framed walls perform and are protected in much the same way; the thickness of the linings is determined by the load to be carried, the cross-section of the studs, cavity filling (if any) and the period of fire resistance required. What is said above, however, relates only to fire resistance. It must be remembered that there may be requirements for non-combustibility as well, as in the case of blocks of flats over four storeys, and in this case the non-combustibility requirement predominates.

When exposed beams or columns of timber are being considered for aesthetic reasons as well as for functional purposes and fire resistance is a requirement, the cross-sections of the members often have to be designed with excess section or 'sacrificial' timber incorporated. This 'sacrificial' material ideally forms part of the solid member but may, in certain circumstances, be planted on. It represents material additional to that required purely for structural purposes and which may be consumed by a fire before the structural core is attacked. Thus, in addition to the many protective layers or measures available to all structural materials, timber has this inherent ability to protect itself.

Timber does not expand significantly under the influence of heat (in fact, it may even shrink slightly) and therefore buildings reliant upon timber for structural purposes are not likely to suffer sudden collapse caused by induced stresses brought about by 'unrestrained' expansion. Timber structures do not collapse suddenly in a fire and timber members will not reach 'breaking point' until they have bent to an alarming extent. In terms of fire, plywood and chipboard sheets used for flooring have an advantage over normal boarding, whether this be plain edged or tongued and grooved. The larger sizes of sheet materials used result in fewer joints, which are usually backed by joists or noggins, and since the joints in flooring represent the weak links in the chain, it follows that, thickness for thickness, the sheet material has a greater resistance to penetration by fire than boarding. Also, plywood or chipboard when applied as lining to partitioning behaves much as plasterboard and provides similar fire resistance. However, to meet the surface spread of flame requirements of the Building Regulations for certain situations (see page 27), these wood-based sheet materials may have to receive appropriate flame retardant treatment.

2 Stone

The types of stone principally employed in building are granite, sandstone and limestone. Igneous rocks, such as granite, contain free quartz, which has the peculiar property of expanding very rapidly at 575°C and completely shattering the rock. Considerable spalling at the surface may occur and thin sections of stone may even disintegrate entirely. When in large solid blocks this effect is limited and is not usually serious. Granite is used chiefly for decorative facings and its failure may not affect the stability of the structure. In some parts of the country, and particularly in Scotland, however, it may be used for load-bearing walls and piers.

Limestones are composed principally of calcium carbonate, which decomposes at about 800°C into free lime and carbon dioxide. The change is gradual with little alteration in volume, and as heat is absorbed in the process, the interior of a block of limestone may be protected by the outer skin. Water used in fire fighting will slake the quicklime so formed and will cause the outer skin to fall away (Plate 1).

Sandstone generally comes between granite and limestone in fire behaviour and may shrink and crack in a fire. Stone is, in general, a good heat insulator, but is inferior to brick when subjected to continuous heat, because of its tendency to spall or split into pieces, especially when water is suddenly applied. Stonework should always be carefully watched for signs of cracking when it is necessary to work beneath or near it.

3 Bricks

Bricks have traditionally been made from clay and similar materials which have been moulded or pressed into shape and fired in a kiln; these are generally referred to as fired-clay bricks. For many years now, concrete bricks and calcium silicate bricks have also been produced. Concrete bricks are made from cement and a fine aggregate, such as sand or a fine crushed stone. Calcium silicate bricks, which are also sometimes known as sand-lime or flint-lime bricks, are made by treating a mixture of lime and a siliceous aggregate in high-pressure steam, the process being known as autoclaving.

Although there are many varieties of each of the three types of brick, and different types of mortar may be used for bedding them, no distinction is made between them in classifying the behaviour of brick walls subjected to a fire on one side. The important features of a brick wall affecting its fire resistance are its thickness, the beneficial effects of applied rendering or plastering, especially lightweight plasters, and whether or not it is load-bearing. Large perforations or cavities in some bricks may make them susceptible to some extent to spalling of small areas of the exposed surfaces.

4 Lime

Lime is used as a component of plaster and mortar and, in older buildings, of concrete. Lime is made by burning limestone (calcium carbonate) and converting it to quicklime which is then slaked (i.e. hydrated). For internal plastered walls, the wall is first rendered

with a coat of lime mortar and then floated with a mixture of lime
and sand to give an even surface.

Given good quality materials and careful application to lathing
or expanded metal with a good key, plaster has good fire-resisting
properties, although it is structurally weak and may easily crack and
fall away.

5 Cement

Cement is a fine powder which reacts chemically with water, and
strength is developed as long as water is available – and not by
drying. Concretes made with the various types of Portland cement
all have similar characteristics when exposed to heat; high-alumina
cement, however, is used for making refractory concretes.

6 Concrete

Concrete consists of aggregates, cement and water which, when first
mixed together form a mouldable material capable of setting and
hardening to produce a solid, rock-like mass with high compressive
strength and great durability. In making concrete it is usual to have
at least two grades of aggregate – coarse and fine – to enable the
quality to be controlled easily. Aggregates may be gravels or crushed
stones or manufactured lightweight aggregates.

When concrete is heated it expands by thermal expansion of the
materials (Plate 2), but the hardened cement paste also shrinks as a
result of loss of moisture by drying out, and the overall change of
size is not easily predicted. Internal stresses can be set up in the concrete which, in severe cases, cause spalling of the surface material;
the risk of spalling may be aggravated if hot concrete is suddenly
chilled by a jet of water. Concretes made with limestone aggregates
or lightweight aggregates (Class 1 aggregates, as for concrete blocks),
are very much less susceptible to spalling than those made with other
dense aggregates, and hence the fire resistance of structural concrete
elements is classified differently according to the type of aggregate
used.

a. Reinforced concrete

Except for concrete bricks and blocks, concrete is rarely used for
structural purposes without being reinforced because it is relatively
weak in tension and prone to crack. In the early days of reinforced
concrete construction, reinforcement consisted of plain round mild
steel bars, but high tensile steel reinforcement – hot rolled bars or
cold-worked bars of different types – have been introduced over the
years. In reinforced concrete, the steel is not stressed until loads are
imposed on the structural member.

b. Pre-stressed concrete

Pre-stressed concrete is a form of structural concrete in which high tensile steel tendons are stressed against the length of the concrete, which is thus put into compression, before imposed loads are applied. Pre-stressed concrete is sub-divided into pre-tensioned and post-tensioned systems.

(1) Pre-tensioned concrete

This has the tendons stretched and anchored independently of the concrete before the concrete is cast around them and allowed to harden; the tendons are then released from their anchorage but, because they are now bonded to the hardened concrete, they are anchored by the concrete and put it into compression.

(2) Post-tensioned concrete

This is cast with ducts through which the tendons are threaded and then stressed after it has hardened, each tendon being anchored against the concrete. The tendons may remain unbonded, but often the space between the tendons and the ducts is grouted so that the tendons become effectively bonded to the concrete and at the same time are protected against corrosion.

No distinction is drawn between the different forms of pre-stressed concrete in assessing their fire resistance.

c. Fire resistance of concrete

The fire resistance of structural concrete, whether reinforced or pre-stressed, is determined primarily by the protection against an excessive rise in the temperature of the steel afforded by the concrete cover, i.e., the concrete between the surface of the member and the nearest surface of the embedded steel. Generally, the greater the amount of cover, the longer is the period of fire resistance. The so-called 'critical' temperature for the steel is about 550°C for mild steel and about 400°C for high tensile steel, but in neither case is there a sudden change in the properties of the steel; these are the temperatures at which they lose about half their cold strength and therefore at which most of the design factor of safety is likely to be used up. Structural concrete in a fire does not normally collapse suddenly – it may deflect considerably under load, and floors may suffer local break-down, but even after a severe fire most concrete structures are safe enough to be reinstated to perform their original functions.

7 Building blocks

Building blocks, like bricks, are used for the construction of walls of all types, and they have become popular because of the savings resulting from the improved productivity when laying units larger than bricks. Specially shaped blocks are also used in floor construction;

these are supported between structural concrete beams, as described in Chapter 4. Blocks are generally made of fired clay or concrete. Hollow-fired clay and concrete blocks are sufficiently different in their fire-resisting properties to be considered separately.

a. Hollow-fired clay blocks

These have relatively thin faces and webs. The blocks are normally laid in non-loadbearing partitions with the axes of their cavities horizontal. They are made with two or three cells across the thickness of the wall and with different proportions of void space to overall volume. Their fire-resisting qualities are generally better the greater the thickness and the smaller the proportion of voids. In a fire, the face of the block exposed to the fire, whether used in a partition or a floor, may spall as a result of the unequal expansion of the material in the block as the temperature rises.

b. Concrete blocks

There are several types of concrete block used for both loadbearing walls and non-loadbearing partitions. Most are moulded by special machines from concrete made with normal dense aggregates or lightweight aggregates; these can be either solid or hollow blocks. Aerated concrete blocks are made by quite a different process, from cement, sometimes lime, and fine siliceous aggregates and a material which causes the formation of numerous small air cells. A large 'cake' is produced which is cut into pieces and autoclaved, like calcium silicate bricks. These blocks are only available as solid blocks.

Concrete blocks are made in a variety of thicknesses; those 51 or 64 mm thick (or more recently 60 and 75 mm thick) are solid and may only be used for non-loadbearing partitions. Those from 75 to 100 mm thick may be solid or hollow and those over 100 mm thick are usually hollow, although solid blocks have been made for carrying unusually high loads. Blocks with a thickness of 75 mm or more may be used for loadbearing or non-loadbearing walls. The cavities in hollow blocks usually have their axes vertical, as laid, which allow the blocks to be reinforced vertically for special loadbearing duties; there is usually only one cavity across the thickness of a block.

The concrete blocks available many years ago were generally made from dense aggregates (Class 2) or from furnace clinker (Class 1); the clinker blocks were often referred to as 'breeze blocks', although only a very small proportion was ever made from proper coke breeze. Both types are still made in large quantities, but blocks are now also made from specially-manufactured lightweight aggregates, produced by some heat treatment, or from natural lightweight aggregate, such as pumice.

c. Fire resistance of concrete blocks

For the purpose of determining fire resistance, machine-made blocks are divided into two classes according to the type of aggregate used in their manufacture. Class 1 blocks – those with the higher fire resistance for a given thickness – are made from lightweight aggregates or from limestone aggregates; Class 2 blocks which, for the same periods of fire resistance, require a slightly greater thickness, are made from natural dense aggregates other than limestone. Slightly different values apply to aerated concrete blocks; compared with Class 1 aggregate blocks, loadbearing walls with 240 or 360 minutes of fire resistance should be a little thicker, but non-loadbearing walls with low periods of resistance can be thinner. All types provide a high degree of fire resistance with little risk of collapse or deterioration and, therefore, give effective compartmentation.

The fire resistance of block walls is improved if they are plastered on both sides and especially so if a lightweight plaster, such as vermiculite-gypsum plaster, is used.

8 Metals

Whilst a number of different metals are used to some extent in building, only iron and steel (and to a limited extent in recent years, aluminium) are normally used for those parts which have to carry any load. Cast iron possesses relatively little strength in tension, but is capable of sustaining a considerable load in compression. Cast iron was very widely used in the 19th century for beams and columns, and even now there are many buildings in use which are supported by cast-iron columns and beams. Iron and steel used in the construction of a building are not combustible and present no risk of fire spread from direct burning. Unprotected metal surfaces may, none the less, constitute a serious risk in a fire because all metals heat up and expand when exposed to fire and are also a potential cause of fire spread by conduction. Unprotected metal which is used to carry a load also presents the even more serious danger of rapid collapse when excessively heated. Structural steel, for example, loses two-thirds of its strength at 593°C and, in proportion to the amount and direction of the load to which it is subjected, begins to sag and twist. This is by no means an abnormal temperature in even a moderate fire, and the danger of unprotected load-bearing metal work cannot be over-emphasised (see Plate 3).

In addition, metals expand when heated. A 10 metres steel joist, for example, will expand 60 mm for a 500°C rise of temperature, and where it is built into a loadbearing wall, such expansion may cause collapse (see Plate 4). In a framed building, the failure of a single beam or column is unlikely to cause more than a local collapse, but nevertheless, it must be emphasised that to be relied on to withstand a fire, structural steel should always be protected by a layer of non-combustible heat-insulating material (see page 43).

Besides the very real danger of distortion and collapse of all metals under heat, cast iron has always had a bad reputation for its behaviour in a fire. It is open to doubt whether this reputation is fully justified for, after many serious fires, cast-iron columns have been found in place when the steelwork has collapsed. When working in the vicinity of cast-iron columns which have been heated (Plate 5), however, it is a wise precaution to avoid playing a jet directly on them because the rapid cooling may cause them to crack and fail suddenly.

Sheet steel is an inexpensive and therefore commonly used form of external weather-resisting cladding, particularly for industrial and warehouse buildings. Because it is prone to rapid corrosion, the steel sheet is invariably coated, normally with a protective metal coating in the first place, and, outside this, frequently with some form of mineral and resin mixture. This is liable to produce the anomaly that, whereas steel sheet itself is non-combustible, a protected steel sheet of the type described may well have a surface spread of flame of Class 1, 2 or even 3.

Increasing use is being made of aluminium and its alloys for structural and cladding members and this has created new fire problems. The advantages of using aluminium alloy in buildings are:

(i)   a reduction in the weight of the structure;
(ii)   resistance to corrosion;
(iii)   ease of handling and working; and
(iv)   the high strength to weight ratio.

The disadvantages are:

(v)   the very rapid loss of strength in fire (stability is affected at 100°C to 225°C);
(vi)   the high expansion rate (approximately twice that of steel);
(vii)   the high thermal conductivity (over three times that of steel); and
(viii) its very low melting point (pure aluminium melts at 660°C).

Lead is principally employed for internal plumbing (although to a lesser extent nowadays), flashings and roof coverings. It melts at 327°C and precautions should therefore be taken against injury from molten metal when working beneath a lead roof at a fire. Copper and zinc are also used for roof coverings but their melting points are much higher and the metal usually oxidises away under the influence of the fire so that there is rarely much danger from falling molten material. Bronze has a melting point about 1000°C, but is normally only used for decorative grilles, handrails, etc. and occasionally for window frames.

9 Glass

Glass is non-combustible and will not, therefore, contribute fuel to a

13

fire or directly assist a fire to spread. Glass may, however, constitute a major weakness in a wall, screen or door, which is intended to act as a barrier to fire because it will break and fall out when exposed to high temperatures.

For fire resistance purposes only two types of glazing are suitable:

a. Wired glass
Wired glass is generally 6 mm thick, either diamond, Georgian or hexagonal mesh (Fig. 1.1(1)).

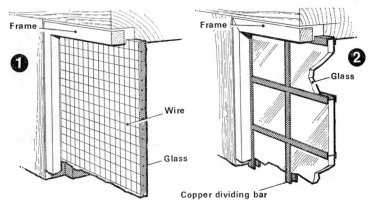

Fig. 1.1 Two types of fire-resisting glazing. (1) wired glass in which the mesh is rolled into the glass during manufacture. (2) copperlight glazing.

b. Copperlight glazing
This consists of panes 6 mm thick and 100 mm square, held together by electrically-deposited copper strips (Fig. 1.1(2)). The co-efficient of expansion of copper is approximately the same as that of glass so that in heat conditions both materials expand at the same rate, holding the composite panel together.

Other types of glass of interest are:

c. Armourplate
This is a type of toughened glass, the surfaces being in tension. (Plate and float glass are different from armourplate, being ordinary glass sheets.) Armourplate is often used for providing frameless doors, but these will have no fire resistance, as the glass is incapable of withstanding temperatures above 300°C.

d. Double glazing
This reduces heat loss by providing double and sometimes triple thicknesses of glass set rigidly in a frame and sealed at the edges.

This does not provide a fire-resisting structure of any kind and the glass is likely to shatter in fire conditions.

e. Glass blocks

These blocks (Fig. 1.2), which are also known as glass bricks, are hollow, translucent glass units having various patterns moulded on their interior or exterior faces, or on both. They are used for internal and exterior wall panels.

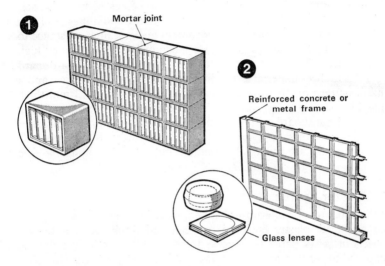

Fig. 1.2 Sketch showing (1) glass blocks and (2) a panel glazed with glass blocks.

10 Building boards

A wide range of materials is used in the manufacture of sheets of varying sizes and thicknesses. They bear many different trade names but may be classified generally in one of the following groups:

    (a) Fibre building boards.
    (b) Plaster boards.
    (c) Asbestos boards.
    (d) Plywood boards.
    (e) Block boards.
    (f) Plastic boards.

a. Fibre building boards

Fibre building boards are manufactured in a wide range of sheet materials, usually more than 1·5 mm thick. They are made from actual wood fibres or woody plants and derive their basic strength and cohesion by the felting together of the fibres themselves, and from their inherent adhesive properties. Bonding, impregnating or other agents, including fire retardants, may be added during or after manufacture to modify particular properties.

Fibre building boards fall into two major groups according to whether the board has been compressed in a hydraulic press during manufacture or not. The non-compressed type is termed insulating board (softboard). This is used both in sheet form and as tiles. Bitumen impregnated insulating board also comes within this category; it is used for sheathing timber-framed buildings and for roof sarking (lining), the bitumen content giving it high resistance to moisture. In the second group are medium boards of low or high density from 6–13 mm thick and hardboards. Standard hardboard is a dense sheet material 2–13 mm thick with one smooth face and a mesh pattern on the reverse. Tempered hardboard, 3–13 mm thick has high strength and water resistance. It is made by impregnating standard hardboard with oils and resins, usually immediately after pressing, and then applying further heat treatment. Building boards of this group are not easily ignitable but all are combustible (see Table 1 on pages 26 and 27).

b. Plaster boards

Plaster boards for interior use are composed of a core of set gypsum or anhydrite plaster enclosed between and firmly bonded to two sheets of heavy paper to increase their tensile strength. In a fire the exposed paper face may burn away making it relatively easy to break up the non-combustible gypsum core, but until this happens, the plaster board will retard the spread of fire.

c. Asbestos boards

Asbestos building boards are manufactured as two distinct types:

(1) Asbestos cement sheets

These consist of between 12 and 15 per cent asbestos, the remainder being cement; this composition will result in the sheet shattering in the early stages of a fire.

(2) Asbestos insulating or wallboard

This is made with an almost completely opposite mix, namely up to 80 per cent asbestos, the remainder being a lime-silica bonding material; this gives the board good fire properties. It is non-combustible, but there is some contraction at high temperatures which tends to bow the material away from the source of heat.

d. Plywood boards

Plywood boards (Fig. 1.3(1)) are made up of thin wood laminations in alternate directions to increase their strength. Their susceptibility to fire depends on the timber used and the thickness of the board. The type of bonding material may have some bearing on the development of a fire.

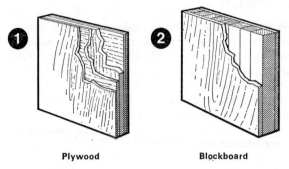

Plywood   **Blockboard**

Fig. 1.3 Diagrams showing the composition of (1) a plywood board, and (2) blockboard.

e. Block boards

These are made from a core of separate wood blocks bonded together (Fig. 1.3(2)), and finished externally with a veneer or plastic overlay to give the appearance of a homogeneous board. They are produced in many grades and qualities and their behaviour in fire varies accordingly.

f. Plastics boards

Plastics boards are composed of organic materials, e.g. paper, linen, sawdust or woodchips, bonded together with synthetic resins and subjected to heat and pressure. Phenolic laminates are rigid boards made of sheets of special paper impregnated with phenol-formaldehyde and urea-formaldehyde. This type of board has good fire-resisting properties and usually incorporates a flame retardant substance in its manufacture. Resin-bonded sawdust (or woodchip) boards are sawdust and/or woodchips bonded with synthetic resins, and are man-made timbers; their behaviour in fire is dependent on their surface treatment.

11 Building slabs

Many of the materials listed in Section 10, 'Building boards' can be increased in thickness and made into more convenient sizes; they are then known as building slabs. Certain materials are made specifically as building slabs. The most common of these are wood-wool slabs and compressed straw slabs. The former are made from wood shavings and cement and the latter from compressed straw

17

sandwiched between heavy paper board. They are often used for roof decking and for sound and heat insulation. They are combustible but can be treated to give improved fire behaviour.

12 Insulating material

In order to reduce heat transmission and to deaden sound, hollow spaces, such as those between double partitions, between an exterior wall and an internal lining or in a floor (Plate 6), are frequently filled with materials which are of a loose fibrous nature and have a low conductivity. Many substances have been used for this purpose, including such combustible materials as cork, sawdust and peat. Modern research, however, has produced non-combustible substitutes such as rock or glass wool, foamed slag, vermiculite, etc., and these are now replacing the older materials in new buildings, although by no means all insulating materials now being employed are non-combustible. Materials of all these types are used extensively in buildings of light construction, such as prefabricated buildings. They are also used in roof construction in industrial buildings which are subject to the provisions of the *Thermal Insulation (Industrial Buildings) Act 1957*, and the Regulations thereunder.

To enable them to be laid rapidly in position, insulating materials are sometimes sandwiched between layers of bituminous paper or felt and are then known as 'quiltings'. Combustible quiltings, e.g. those with a wood or seaweed base, enable a fire to travel easily through concealed wall and ceiling spaces, the plaster or board lining preventing effective extinction until it is removed.

A form of insulating material specially developed for incorporating fire resistance into elements of structure is known as *sprayed asbestos*. This consists of an asbestos mixture which is pumped in a liquid state under pressure through hose and discharged as a spray on to beams, columns, floors, etc. It sets hard with time, and represents a quick and easy method of creating fire resistance: a typical value is $1\frac{1}{2}$ hours' protection from 25 mm of sprayed asbestos. This is a form of fire protection which for its effectiveness depends much on the quality of workmanship in the application. Another feature is the risk that sprayed asbestos cladding may be dislodged or damaged by mechanical action, by vibration or by differential expansion between two faces.

13 Paint

Paint is used both as a preservative and as a decoration principally for woodwork and steelwork, but is sometimes applied to plaster or brickwork. Paint consists of a pigment (normally a powdered solid) carried in a vehicle (a liquid) which by chemical action and evaporation allows the film to harden. Almost all paints (with the exception of fire-retardant paints mentioned later) are flammable, but the film

Plate 1. An example of the spalling of limestone when subjected to heat and subsequently to cooling by a jet.

Plate 2. An example of spalling of concrete of the surface material. Note the protection of the steelwork by the asbestos insulation board remaining intact.

Plate 3. The severe effect of heat on unprotected steelwork

Plate 4. The result of expansion of unprotected universal steel sections inside a building causing displacement of the brickwork.

Plate 5. The effect of a severe fire on unprotected cast iron columns and universal steel sections.

Plate 6. The insulating material filling in a void in a building.

Plate 7. Fire propagation test apparatus showing the specimen holder and the calibration board in place. The gas burner can be seen in the apparatus near the bottom with the electric heaters above.

Plate 8. The apparatus used for a large scale surface spread of flame test.

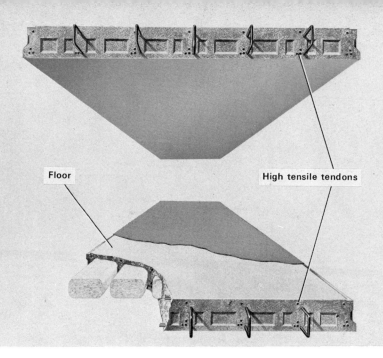

Floor

High tensile tendons

Plate 9. One method of construction of a unit of prestressed concrete. Note the ends of the high tensile tendons which appear as black dots.

Plate 10. The manner in which a wattle-and-daub wall was constructed.

Plate 11.   Prestressed concrete planks.

Plate 12.   A finished prestressed concrete plank floor also shown is the channelling into which prestressed concrete planks are positioned.

Plate 13. A view of the space between queen posts of a queen post truss utilised as a storage area.

Plate 14. A prime example of cast iron roof trusses and cast iron columns. Note the north light roofing upper right.

Plate 15. A typical simple batten and slate roof construction showing the burnt roof timbers having allowed the slates to slide and provide ventilation.

Plate 16. A 17th-century roof structure showing some remaining tile battens and fallen tiles as a result of fire.

ordinarily is so thin that it has no appreciable effect on a fire, although under certain conditions, it can foster surface spread. Sometimes, however, when many coats of paint have been applied over a number of years, the film may be sufficiently thick to become flammable and constitute a fire risk. The paint on steelwork, for instance, can ignite if heated sufficiently by a fire, e.g. the far side of a bulkhead in a ship fire. Where appearance is unimportant, tar or bituminous paint is sometimes used and the film may then be sufficiently thick to burn even though applied to steelwork with no other combustible material present.

Fire-retardant paints are occasionally used to protect timber and are of two types. One type is a fairly heavy-based paint which will not inhibit combustion completely, but will do much to reduce flaming, whilst the other, which is termed an 'intumescent paint', will, when subjected to heat, bubble up and form a layer of air cells which acts as an insulation between the heat of the fire and the timber underneath. This type of paint is very effective and can be obtained in colour or as a transparent covering.

14 Plastics

Reference has already been made in Section 10(f) to 'Plastics boards', but with the increasing use of plastics materials in the building industry, it is appropriate to make a further general reference to these materials.

The term 'plastics' (which, it should be noted, can be used as a noun, both singular and plural, and as an adjective), is a generic name for a group of materials based on synthetic or modified natural polymers (see the *Manual, Book 1, Chapter 9*) which at some stage of manufacture can be formed to shape by flow, aided in many cases by heat and pressure. They can be *thermosetting*, i.e. they will not soften significantly on heating to a temperature below decomposition temperature, or *thermoplastic*, i.e. capable of being softened by the application of heat.

Plastics materials of different degrees of stiffness are described as rigid, semi-rigid and non-rigid plastics. *Reinforced plastics* consist essentially of polymer combined with fibrous material to enhance its mechanical strength. This term is most commonly used for thermosetting polyester resin with glass fibre (GRP). One of the uses of this material is as external cladding in the form of moulded panels in building systems. *Cellular plastics* are made up of a mass of cells in which the matrix is a plastics material. *Foamed plastics* are cellular plastics made mainly from liquid-starting materials, e.g. polyurethane foam. *Expanded plastics* are made by stamping or cutting plastics sheet and stretching to form open meshes, in the same way as expanded metal is formed.

The problems of tensile and comprehensive strengths of these materials for their possible use as structural elements have not yet been fully resolved and, except for small complete structures, they are not used for loadbearing members. A substantial amount of plastics material will, however, be encountered within buildings in the form of thermal insulation, service pipes, wall, floor and ceiling covering, furniture, furnishings and fitments. Translucent sheets are used for rooflights where the relevant Building Regulations allow.

Plastics materials cover such a wide range of substances that their properties and behaviour in fire can be described only in very broad terms. Most plastics will burn to a greater or lesser degree dependent on the bulk of the material, the free access to air and any support to combustion that may be available. The products of combustion of many plastics materials may be very toxic; it must however be borne in mind that this also applies to a greater or lesser extent to the combustion of all other materials.

Further information on the subject of fires involving plastics is contained in the *Manual, Part 6C: Chapter 45, Section 10* (Book No. 15 in the new format).

Chapter 2
Fire testing of materials

This chapter describes those of the environmental tests set out in *British Standard 476* which are applicable to materials, but not to elements of structure, as the fire tests for these are dealt with in Part 2. British Standard 476 is published in a number of parts: those dealing with building materials are:

BS 476   Part 4: 1970   Non-combustibility test for materials
BS 476   Part 5: 1968   Ignitability test for materials
BS 476   Part 6: 1968   Fire propagation test for materials
BS 476   Part 7: 1971   Surface spread of flame tests for materials

In describing the material tests under BS 476, indications are given in this chapter of the qualities which each test is designed to cover or clarify, and the types of fire situation to which the tests are presumed to relate.

When studying the technique of fire testing, the reader should keep in mind the object of such tests and their relationship to the system of building control embodied in, for instance, the Building Regulations. It can never be the object of a fire test to study, or even to judge, the acceptability of building materials. One cannot look to the results of these tests to know whether a material is satisfactory or not, and one should not think of the tests in this way. The acceptability of a material depends on a great number of extraneous factors as well as on the qualities of the material itself; principally, it depends on the level of fire risk to life inherent in the situation in which the material is used. Thus, a material showing certain flame-spread characteristics may be satisfactory – and acceptable – when used in the roof of a single storey factory, but not in an escape corridor of a place of public assembly. In each case someone, or some authority, has to make a subjective assessment of the risks involved and decide that a given material does or does not enable the desired standard of safety to be attained. This assessment may assist in the framing of Regulations or in granting relaxations from them. The test will not of itself reveal whether it does; it will only forecast the probable behaviour of the material. This forecast is meaningless until placed against the background of a set standard of safety. As an example, let us say that a certain type of board is proposed for use as a decorative wall panelling. Its suitability for this is judged (if fire resistance is not involved – see Part 2) by the surface spread of flame test. In this test, the board obtains a rating of Class 2. The board can in fact be used in some situations in a building but not in others, and only reference to Part E of the Building Regulations 1972 (England and Wales) or its equivalent in Scotland, will reveal the situations in which it may be used.

The results of fire tests, however, are not only used for purposes of building control and regulation. Insurance companies, through the Fire Offices' Committee, use them for regulating premiums, and they may equally well be used in specifications for purchase and in other ways. In all instances the same rule applies: the test does not of itself decide the material's acceptability; it only measures its qualities.

1 British standard tests

The principal criteria for assessing the fire properties of building products are, as has already been said, to be found in the tests set out in BS 476. These standard methods of test are referred to in the Building Regulations and are used by the Joint Fire Research Organisation and other laboratories as the basis for fire testing of building products. BS 476 gives general indications, but does not define which products should be tested or by which tests, nor is it concerned with laying down requirements for particular situations. Its sole purpose is to define the means and the procedure whereby the fire properties of building products may be studied and graded.

It should not be assumed from this that the tests incorporated in BS 476 are regarded in any permanent sense as covering all the fire properties of building materials which are of interest. BS 476 has been built up over the years against a background of continuous, and recently increasing, research activity into the nature of fire and its behaviour as a phenomenon. Many possible forms of test, capable of specifying many different fire properties, are currently being investigated and the present content of BS 476 represents the stage which has currently been reached, but not necessarily a true reflection of the fire properties which need to be tested. The tests which have already been devised and are currently incorporated in the Standard cover the following main properties which influence the behaviour of building materials when involved in fire:

(i) combustibility;
(ii) ignitability;
(iii) fire propagation; and
(iv) rate of surface spread of flame.

BS 476 is not the only Standard containing tests which is referred to in the Building Regulations. In particular connections, such as the determination of the relative temperatures of melting and ignition possessed by plastics materials used as rooflights, certain other test standards are referred to, such as BS 2782.

2 Non-combustibility test for materials

Materials are said to be combustible if they are capable of under-going combustion, i.e., being consumed by oxidation, with the production of heat, usually with incandescence or flame or both.

British Standard 476: Part 4: 1970 specifies a non-combustibility test for materials. The term *non-combustibility* is used instead of *combustibility* following joint investigation and discussion in an international context and is in line with proposals of the International Standards Organisation (ISO). The test determines simply whether building materials are non-combustible or combustible. The material tested shall be deemed to be non-combustible if, whilst in a furnace heated to 750°C for 20 minutes, none of three specimens, each measuring 40 mm wide by 40 mm long by 50 mm high, i.e. occupying a volume of 80 cubic centimetres, either:

(i) causes the temperature reading from either of two thermo-couples to rise by 50°C or more above the initial furnace temperature; or

(ii) is observed to flame for 10 seconds or more inside the furnace.

Otherwise, the material shall be deemed to be combustible.

It should be noted that materials less than 50 mm thick will be tested in layers up to that thickness. For practical purposes it should be appreciated that, by suitably adjusting conditions, many materials thought of as being non-combustible, can be made to burn, e.g. iron and steel in oxygen.

3 Ignitability test for materials

Some materials can be more easily ignited than others; celluloid, for example, ignites readily, but wood less easily, although the ignitability of wood depends on whether the wood is in the form of shavings or thicker timber. *British Standard 476: Part 5: 1968* specifies a test which classifies combustible material as 'easily ignitable' (Classification X) or 'not easily ignitable' (Classification P). The test is intended for rigid or semi-rigid building materials but is not suitable for fabrics, for which separate tests are specified.

Each of the three specimens submitted for test is successively held vertically over a controlled gas jet for 10 seconds, the jet is then removed and a note made of the subsequent flaming, if any, to the nearest second. If any of the three specimens flames for more than 10 seconds after the removal of the test flame, *or* if burning of the specimen extends to the edge within 10 seconds, the material is classified as 'easily ignitable' and its performance is indicated by the letter 'X'. If none of the three specimens flames for more than 10 seconds after the removal of the test flame and burning does not extend to the edge within this time, the material is classified as 'not easily ignitable' and its performance is indicated by the letter 'P'.

The size of the test specimens must be 228 mm square and of the same thickness as the material which they represent.

4 Fire propagation test for materials

Investigation into the growth of fires in buildings shows that the surface spread of flame test does not indicate the only measurable properties which are necessary for placing lining materials in their proper order of hazard. Account must also be taken of the amount and rate of heat evolved by a material whilst it is being subjected to heat in an enclosed space. *British Standard 476: Part 6: 1968* details the procedure for testing building materials for fire propagation. The test result is given as a 'Performance Index'. This provides a comparative measure of the contribution a material will make to heat build-up and thus to fire spread within a compartment. Values may range in ascending order of merit from 0 upwards. This is termed the 'I' index. The test apparatus (Fig. 2.1) is first calibrated by testing with asbestos board and so obtaining a calibration curve.

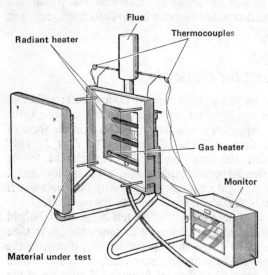

Fig. 2.1 The fire propagation test apparatus as shown in BS 476: Part 6: 1968.

A sample of the material to be tested is inserted in the specimen holder (Plate 7) and the temperature rise of the flue gases throughout a 20-minute test is recorded. Readings are taken at $\frac{1}{2}$-minute intervals for the first 3 minutes, the result being given as 'Sub-index i_1', then at 1-minute intervals from 4 to 10 minutes, under 'Sub-index i_2' and finally at 2-minute intervals from 12 to 20 minutes, under 'Sub-index i_3'. Examination of the specimen values as compared with the calibration curve of the three sub-indices reveal different properties of the material being assessed. The use of the initial component 'i_1' is an indication of the ignitability and flammability of the material. The sum total of the sub-indices indicates the heat contribution a particular material makes to a fire.

The performance indices for various materials are given in Table 1 and show the behaviour in fire of some typical products. It must be emphasised that these should not be regarded as applicable to all materials of that type; indeed many are improved by fire retardant treatments. The fire propagation test is incomplete without the addition of a report and classification from the ignitability test. Tests are currently being devised to assess materials for smoke evolution and toxic gas content. These tests will probably be issued as extensions of the existing fire propagation test.

The choice of performance limits for various situations will progressively evolve and will be set out in the Building Regulations. These will be accepted commercially in a way similar to that in which other British Standards relating to fire tests have become commonplace.

The *Building Regulations 1972* quote two situations which mention the fire propagation test. These are:

(i) When considering cladding on an external wall below a height of 15 metres from the ground and 1 metre or more from the boundary, timber of not less than 10 mm may be used, or a material which, when tested in accordance with the prescribed fire propagation test, has an index of performance 'I' not exceeding 20.

(ii) In a reference to Class 0 materials (see Section 5(b) below), the surface material (or, if bonded throughout to a substrate, the surface material and substrate combined), shall have an index performance 'I' not exceeding 12 and a sub-index i_1 not exceeding 6.

It will be noted that in the first situation (i) above, the sub-index i_1 is not quoted. From Table 1 it will be seen that typical materials for use in this situation could be impregnated fibre insulating board, a flame-retardant grade of melamine phenolic laminate, sheet steel or many other materials. In the second situation (ii) above, such materials as a flame-retardant grade of glass-reinforced polyester resin (GRP), mineral fibre tiles and woodwool slab, amongst other materials, could be acceptable providing all other requirements of the Regulations in respect of fitness of material for particular functions are satisfied.

Table 1

Performance indices for typical materials

Material	Treatment/facing	Thickness mm	I	i_1	i_2+i_3
Wood and wood-based materials					
Fibre insulating board	–	13	66·4	41·0	25·4
Softwood	–	18	42·5	17·2	25·3
Fibre insulating board	Emulsion painted	13	42·0	18·0	24·0
Plywood	–	6	41·2	19·5	21·7
Hardboard	Stove-enamelled coating	9	37·3	13·5	23·8
Particle board	–	18	36·3	12·8	23·5
Hardwood	–	19	34·9	9·5	25·4
Hardboard	–	5	30·1	10·5	19·6
Semi-compressed hardboard	Plastics coated	13	24·3	5·5	18·8
Hardboard	Impregnated	5	24·3	7·2	17·1
Fibre insulating board	Intumescent flame-retardant coating	13	20·0	5·9	14·1
Fibre insulating board	Impregnated	13	18·4	6·4	12·0
Softwood	Flame-retardant varnish	19	18·1	4·9	13·2
Fibre insulating board	Asbestos paper faced	13	16·5	3·8	12·7
Hardboard	Intumescent flame-retardant coating	5	16·4	4·0	12·4
Softwood	Intumescent flame-retardant coating	19	15·1	5·8	9·3
Plastics-based materials					
Expanded rubber	–	51	99·8	80·1	19·7
Polyether foam	–	51	88·6	68·4	20·2
Acrylic sheet	–	3	39·8	20·0	19·8
Polyurethane foam	Flame-retardant grade	35	38·7	27·3	11·4
Melamine-faced hardboard	–	6	32·3	12·4	19·9
Expanded polystyrene	Standard grade	25	29·4	22·1	7·3
Polyurethane foam	Flame-retardant grade	13	28·6	23·4	5·2
Glass-reinforced polyester resin	–	3	26·4	10·4	16·0
Melamine phenolic laminate	Flame-retardant grade	2	18·3	5·4	12·9
Glass-reinforced polyester	Inert filler finish	5	16·9	5·5	11·4
Polyvinyl chloride	–	3	16·8	5·9	10·9
Glass-reinforced polyester resin	Flame-retardant grade	3	11·2	4·0	7·2
Expanded polystyrene	Self-extinguishing grade	13	10·1	7·1	3·0
Melamine phenolic laminate	Flame-retardant grade	2	7·2	1·5	5·7

Material	Treatment/facing	Thickness mm	I	i_1	$i_2 + i_3$
Coated non-combustible sheet materials					
Asbestos board	Wood veneer > 0·8 mm thick	19	22·2	12·2	10·0
Steel sheet	Resin-coated impregnated asbestos	3	11·9	3·9	8·0
Asbestos board	Polyvinyl chloride film 0·4 mm thick	9	7·4	5·1	2·3
Steel sheet	Polyvinyl chloride coat 0·3 mm thick	1	5·5	2·2	3·3
Steel sheet	Painted, one coat	1	1·7	1·3	0·4
Mineral and glass fibre wool, tiles, etc.					
Mineral fibre tile with organic binder	Emulsion paint coat	22	16·6	7·7	8·9
Glass fibre, resin-bonded, on steel sheet	Neoprene coated	25	10·5	5·0	5·5
Mineral fibre tile with plaster, resin-bonded	–	19	9·8	5·0	4·8
Glass fibre, resin-bonded, on steel sheet	–	25	9·6	5·1	4·5
Mineral fibre tile, organic binder	–	13	8·1	4·6	3·5
Glass fibre, resin-bound	–	25	7·5	3·6	3·9
Mineral fibre, resin-bonded	–	25	6·5	4·1	2·4
Miscellaneous materials					
Woodwool slab (high density)	–	25	11·5	5·2	6·3
Woodwool slab (low density)	–	51	10·3	5·2	5·1
Plasterboard	Polyvinyl chloride facing 0·2 mm	9·5	10·0	5·4	4·6
Plasterboard	–	13	9·9	5·8	4·1
Plasterboard	–	9·5	9·7	5·7	4·0
Plasterboard	Emulsion painted	13	9·0	5·2	3·8

Note: Values given in this table are indicative of performance indices likely to be obtained from different types of lining and treatments. They are not intended to be used as values for specific materials.

5 Rate of surface spread of flame

Materials used for wall and ceiling linings have a substantial effect on the way in which a fire will spread. The determination of the tendency of materials to support the spread of flame across their surface is of importance. British Standard 476: Part 7: 1971 specifies two tests to determine the tendency of materials to support the spread of flame: (a) a large-scale test and (b) a small-scale test.

a. The large-scale test

This is intended for the classification of the exposed surfaces of walls and ceilings according to the rate and distance of spread of flame across them (Plate 8). The specimen to be tested is placed in a holder set at an angle of 90 degrees to a radiating furnace panel (Fig. 2.2).

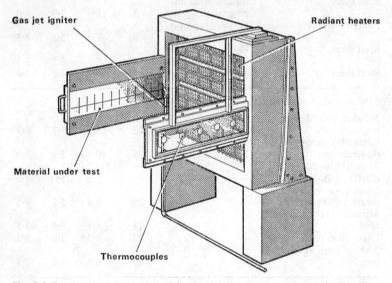

Gas jet igniter

Radiant heaters

Material under test

Thermocouples

Fig. 2.2 The large-scale spread of flame test apparatus as shown in BS 476: Part 7: 1971.

A gas flame is applied at the furnace end of the specimen for 1 minute and is then removed. The distance of the spread of flame is recorded at the end of $1\frac{1}{2}$ minutes. Measurements of flame spread distance against time are continued up to a total time of 10 minutes, unless the flame reaches the far end of the specimen in a shorter time. The material is then classified into one of four classes as shown in Table 2; it will be seen that Class 1 materials show the lowest and Class 4 the highest rate of flame spread. It will also be seen that a tolerance is allowed, i.e. the flame spread may exceed the limit by the amount shown, but only for one specimen in the sample being tested.

b. Small-scale test

The British Standard also specifies a small-scale surface spread of flame test. This is performed on apparatus one-third the linear size of the large-scale apparatus, and the test samples are correspondingly smaller. There is no direct correlation between the two tests; the

Table 2

Flame spread classification

Classification	Flame spread at $1\frac{1}{2}$ minutes		Final flame spread	
	Limit	Tolerance for 1 specimen in sample	Limit	Tolerance for 1 specimen in sample
	mm	mm	mm	mm
Class 1	165	25	165	25
Class 2	215	25	455	45
Class 3	265	25	710	75
Class 4	Exceeding Class 3 limits			

small-scale test is not intended to replace the standard test, but is considered suitable as a test in the development of a product, and for quality control of materials of established properties.

The *Building Regulations 1972* and the *Building Standards (Scotland) (Consolidation) Regulations 1970* refer to materials of Class 0 and Grade A respectively. These specifications call for a different standard from that prescribed by Class 1 in BS 476: Part 7: 1971. Any reference, however, to Class 0 or Grade A materials must be regarded as the highest class followed in descending order by Classes 1, 2, 3 and 4.

6 Test certificates

Following the tests at recognised laboratories, a certificate is issued giving the result of the test(s). In the case of the Joint Fire Research Organisation, this bears a reference number preceded by the letters FROSI (Fire Research Organisation Special Investigation, e.g. Test Certificate FROSI No. . .).

The increase of new building products combined with the increasing number of statutory and other requirements aimed at controlling fires in buildings means that the test facilities are much in demand. However, so much experience has been gained by the testing authorities that in many cases they are able to predict results. In some cases a 'Letter of Assessment' is issued which is normally accepted by building authorities. Manufacturers of building products can obtain advice in the early stages of development, thus ensuring that new products will stand a reasonable chance of satisfying the various test criteria in due course.

Part 2
Elements of structure

In Part 1 a study was made of the behaviour and testing of building materials in fire as a logical first step in considering fires in buildings. Such a study will reveal much about the effects and growth of a fire in a room, for instance, but it will be seriously lacking as an indication of the ultimate fate of a whole burning building. This is because, although we speak of a building being built of concrete or brick, the safety of the building as a whole in fire depends on the way in which the concrete, brick or other materials are used to give it strength and stability. The building is in fact built of elements of structure: beams, columns, walls, floors and so forth. These will have to be tested and controlled; indeed, these tests which all relate to the quality of fire resistance, are in a way an environmental test of the materials of which the elements are composed.

It should be emphasised at this point, in case it has not already become clear, that there are some qualities of materials which cannot be satisfactorily judged in terms of the materials alone, and resistance to fire is a combination of them. There are many simple examples of this. Wood, for instance: a 3-ply sheet is hardly capable of resisting fire, being engulfed by it with great rapidity, but a timber frame may be constructed which will keep a building standing after two hours of intense fire within it. Thin steel sheet cannot long resist fire, as it quickly becomes red hot, transferring the heat of the fire through it, and also becomes buckled and displaced. But a combination of steel sheet and asbestos fibres will make a door capable of resisting fire for two hours. The result of this in practice is that it is meaningless to speak of the fire resistance of a material; testing for fire resistance can be done only on elements of structure, and this is the main subject of this Part of this *Manual*. It also deals with an analogous type of test for roofs, and with the hazards to firemen of elements of structure generally.

Elements of structure is a term which requires elucidation. In its general sense it means one of a number of features of building construction: the examples of beams, columns, walls and floors have already been quoted. However, the phrase has been adopted in Building Regulations in a narrower sense as expressing only a short specified list of such features. The distinction lies really between those elements which are an integral part of the structure of a building as a whole and those which, while still being structural in nature, do not contribute to the overall stability of the building. One needs only to compare a column, for example, with a staircase; the column will be holding up the building, while the staircase is in fact held up by it. Both are structural features, but the column figures in the Building Regulations list as an element of structure, while the staircase does not. The underlying reason for the distinction is, as has been implied, the difference in the nature and importance of the contribution made by the element to the building's stability.

This Part of the *Manual* accepts the distinction in the use of these terms and is laid out accordingly.

Chapter 3
General notes on elements of structure

1 Building Regulations: structural fire precautions

When dealing with the construction of buildings, it is necessary to make frequent reference to the Building Regulations. Although these Regulations mainly concern architects and builders, the fireman in pursuit of his work must have a working knowledge of the 'fire section' of the Regulations. Later in his career, a more thorough knowledge of those parts of the Regulations which deal with all forms of structural fire protection will be necessary, when he will be required to give expert advice on a wide range of subjects dealing with fire prevention and fire protection to other professions allied to the construction industry, to owners and occupiers of premises and to the general public.

The *Building Regulations 1972* of England and Wales are made under powers conferred on the Secretary of State for the Environment by the *Public Health Act, 1936*, as amended by the *Public Health Act, 1961* and by the *Clean Air Act, 1956*. They were produced after consultation with a Building Regulations Advisory Committee (a standing committee of experts) and a group of assessors representing a wide range of interests; they are therefore the culmination of many years of progressive building standards. In law, the fire regulations are included to safeguard the public in and around buildings and not the property or its contents. It naturally follows, however, that ensuring the safety of persons within and about the building must make a valuable contribution towards the protection of the property against the destructive effects of fire.

Many buildings are difficult to classify in terms of a fixed set of Regulations, and the limitations imposed by the latter are sometimes therefore unjustified. In these cases, the procedure is to apply for a relaxation of the appropriate Regulations and there is a power for the Building Authority in the locality to relax the Regulations if it sees fit. However, the Secretary of State for the Environment has reserved to his Department the right to relax certain cases, which include buildings exceeding 7100 cubic metres in volume, town centre redevelopment schemes, air-supported structures and certain other specialised types of building. The Regulations, under powers conveyed in the Fire Precautions Act, 1971 also contain requirements for means of escape.

To understand the structural fire precautions section of the Regulations, it is necessary to be familiar with the terminology used (non-combustible, surface spread of flame, etc.), in order to appreciate the limitations imposed on a structure or finishing material, and to know that the Regulations accept or reject a material or element of structure on the basis of its performance under the tests set out in British Standard 476, some of which have been explained in Chapter 2.

The Regulations do not apply to existing buildings unless an actual change of use of the building is proposed. The Regulations are enforced by the Building Regulation Authorities, which from April 1974 are the District Councils and Outer London Borough Councils. Scotland, Northern Ireland and Inner London have similar but separate enactments to control the construction of buildings.

2 Definition of elements of structure

The Building Regulations define elements of structure as being:

(i) any member forming part of the structural frame of a building (Fig. 3.1(1)), or any other beam or column (2) not being a member forming part of a roof structure only;

(ii) a floor (3), other than the lowest floor of the building;

(iii) an external wall (4);

(iv) a separating wall (5);

(v) a compartment wall (6);

(vi) a structure enclosing a protected shaft (7);

(vii) a load-bearing wall or load-bearing part of a wall (8);

(viii) a gallery (9).

The essential framework of any type of structure can be found by these elements, and they are dealt with in Chapter 4. The other elements, such as stairs, roofs, partitions, etc. which are also necessary to complete a building for occupation, are detailed in Chapter 5.

The function of each of the elements of structure in the majority of buildings is to carry the loads placed upon them. These loads are principally:

(i) The 'dead load', which is the weight of all the parts of the building itself which is imposed upon the elements. These are constant.

(ii) The 'imposed load', which consists of the people, furniture, machinery and materials expected to be in the building when it is occupied. These loads are variable.

(iii) The 'wind load', which means all loads due to the effects of wind pressure or suction.

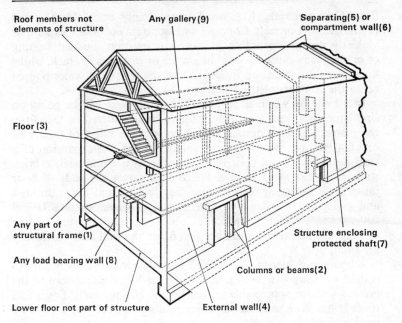

Fig. 3.1 Sketch showing the various elements of structure of a building.

Complex design calculations are necessary to resolve these loadings and a factor of safety is applied to ensure that only materials and elements of structure of sufficient strength and adequate stability are used in construction. The existence of a factor of safety in all well-built structures is useful to the fireman who, by experience, may be able to judge within limits the extent to which the factor of safety has been reduced by burning or distortion of various parts of the building. By an assessment of the remaining factor of safety the fireman may be able to decide whether it is safe to work, in a fire, underneath parts of the structure which have been partially destroyed. It may happen, for example, that a wooden beam may have been considerably burned and charred and yet retain a sufficient factor of safety to allow fire fighting to proceed beneath it without danger; or that, by the destruction of some supports, a beam has been turned into a cantilever which still retains sufficient strength for the fireman's safety. Walls and columns have to carry not only the vertical loads, but also have to withstand the over-turning effects imposed by wind loads and by eccentric loading (i.e. when the beam end is not placed centrally over its supporting member).

The importance of these points to the fireman is that in a fire many of the stresses in a building structure are altered; for heat affects building materials in a number of different ways. Readily flammable materials, like wood, may simply burn. Metals may expand, distort or melt. Concrete and stone may contract, expand or violently disrupt according to their composition. Sudden heating or cooling may cause material like stone or cast iron to crack, whilst floor loads are increased by debris and the weight of water poured on to the contents of the building.

In a building which is on fire all these changes will be going on simultaneously, and a further factor to be considered is, therefore, the interaction of materials, that is to say, the effect of failure of one material on the strength of another. Thus, the expansion of a steel beam may cause collapse of an otherwise sound wall; a brick wall may twist away from a fire and let down the ends of floor joists built into it, or the converse may happen and burnt through and collapsing wooden floor joists, which originally gave lateral stiffening to a wall, may reduce the wall's resistance to wind-loading or may, by their levering action, pull down the wall into which they are built.

A building reduced to its simplest essentials may usually be said to consist of: foundations to transmit the load of the structure to the ground without appreciable movement or shifting; walls, floors and roof. It has been said that a structure does not become a building until it possesses a roof.

3 Fire tests of elements of construction (general)

Details of some of the various tests contained in BS 476 have been described in Chapter 2. These relate to the characteristics of the more common building materials, namely, the substances from which the walls, floors, beams, etc. are made. In order to proceed a stage further, the terms 'elements of structure' and 'fire resistance' are now considered. These terms relate to complete elements and not simply to the materials from which they are made.

Part 8 of BS 476 gives details of the fire tests required for elements of structure and methods by which fire resistance is determined. Dependent upon the function of the element, it has to satisfy one or more of the following criteria:

(i) *Stability*, i.e. the ability of the specimen tested to withstand deformation or collapse.

(ii) *Integrity*, i.e. the ability to withstand cracking or opening up to the extent of allowing flames to pass through.

(iii) *Insulation*, i.e. the ability of the face of the element not exposed to heat to remain comparatively cool.

The specimen under test is progressively heated in an accurately controlled furnace, the temperature of which varies with time as closely as possible to an international standard. This is set out in graph form (Fig. 3.2) and is called the *time-temperature curve*. The heat evolved is not necessarily that which is produced in a true fire situation but is an agreed standard for purposes of comparison. It will be seen from the graph that after 30 minutes the temperature of the furnace is 821°C, increasing to 925°C after 60 minutes, then to 1029°C after 120 minutes to a maximum 1193°C after 360 minutes. These figures illustrate how stringent these performance tests are in respect of elements of structure.

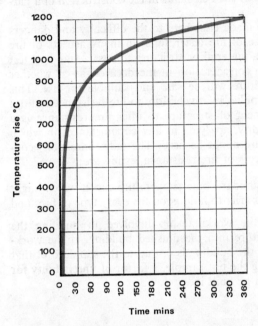

Fig. 3.2 British Standard 476 Part 8: the standard time-temperature curve for fire tests on building materials and structures.

The fire resistance of an element is the time in minutes from the start of the test until failure occurs under any one of the criteria set out in (i) to (iii) above if all are appropriate to the particular type of element being tested; or, if no failure occurs, until the test is terminated.

For example, a test result showing:

Stability: 120
Integrity: 120
Insulation: 15

would mean that a specimen failed in respect of insulation after 15 minutes, but complied with the other criteria for at least 120 minutes.

37

A large number of various types of elements of structure have been tested over a period of years. The designer of a building can therefore refer quite readily to previous test results from a range of official publications and will know whether or not the particular type of construction selected will be appropriate in respect of the fire resistance of the proposed elements of structure. Should he wish to use new or untested materials, testing would be necessary and a satisfactory report would need to be furnished prior to approval being given for the use of such elements in the construction of a particular building.

Reference has been made elsewhere to the difficulty and dangers associated with the use of fire test results; in many aspects of fire testing, the ability of a material or structure to pass a standard test may be only a minor consideration in the decision as to whether that material or structure will be safe and suitable for use. This limitation, however, applies relatively little to fire resistance testing: the ability of an element of structure to offer fire resistance is a relatively positive quality, applying in any circumstances in which the element of structure might be used. The only 'unreliable' considerations in the process of fire resistance testing are:

(i) reliance on the standard time-temperature curve, which might be said not necessarily to hold good for every type of fire; and

(ii) the quality of the workmanship involved in building the element of structure into the finished building. If the workmanship used in the building is not up to the standard of that used in preparing the test sample, a factor of unreliability for the structure can be built in.

4 Terminology

In a brief account such as this, every effort has been made to avoid the unnecessary use of technical terms, and it should be explained that for simplicity of reference, the words 'column' and 'beam' have been used throughout to indicate respectively vertical and horizontal load-bearing members generally, irrespective of the material from which they are made or the positions in which they are used. Architects and builders however, vary the terms used in accordance partially with the material employed and partially with the function it is called upon to perform, and a list of the generally used terms is given in Table 3 so that the fireman may be able to recognise them when reading other technical works.

When a beam is used to span a short distance over an opening (e.g. a door or window) it is generally termed a lintel, but when it carries a load such as a wall over a larger opening (e.g. the wall above a shop front) it is sometimes termed a bressumer, although

Table 3

Material	When used as a column	When used as a beam
Stone	Pier, column or pillar	Lintel, arch
Brick	Pier or pilaster	Arch or flat arch
Timber	Post or strut	Joist, lintel, bearer, beam, rafter
Steel	Stanchion, strut or column, roof member, Universal steel section	Joist, universal steel section, beam, lintel, truss.
Wrought or cast iron	Column	Beam, girder, lintel
Reinforced concrete	Column	Beam, lintel

this word is falling into disuse. The relative appearance of a lintel and a beam serving as a bressumer are shown in Fig. 3.3.

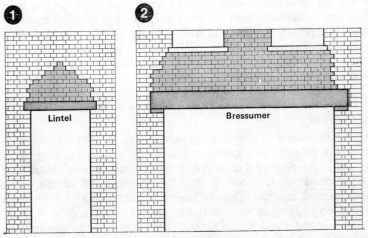

Fig. 3.3 Sketches showing the difference between (1) a lintel and (2) a bressumer. The shading indicates the load carried.

Chapter 4
True elements of structure

1 Columns

The function of a column is to carry a part of the weight of the building where an internal wall would interfere with the use of a building, or where a large open space is needed. A column (which in this connection may be considered as replacing a load-bearing wall) is often designed to withstand only vertical loads. Any eccentric load greatly increases the stress and will overturn any column not rigidly fixed at the foot.

The six principal materials which have been used for the construction of columns are: timber, brick, stone, reinforced and pre-stressed concrete, cast iron and steel. Of these, timber, brick and stone were in general use until about 1800; cast iron was almost universally employed in the 19th century whilst steel, reinforced concrete and laminated timber are modern materials.

a. Timber

At the beginning of the 19th century, timber posts were normally used for columns in multi-storey factories and mills. They were spaced at intervals of 8 to 10 ft (2·5 to 3 metres) in rows about 15 ft (4·5 metres) apart. Some of these factories are still in use, often incorporated into buildings of later construction which have been added on to them at various times. Timber columns (Fig. 4.1) are usually found fitted with cast-iron caps which accommodate the ends of the wooden beams. When columns are located one above the other on the various floors, a cast-iron pintle (a bar of round section) runs through the beam in line with the column and transmits the load from the column above to that below in order to avoid placing an undue crushing force on the intervening woodwork. (See also the remarks on timber under Section 2, 'Beams' on page 46.)

b. Laminated timber

Techniques for laminating sections of timber (Fig. 4.2(1)) are now well-established and often replace the more costly baulks of timber described in (a) above. These are referred to descriptively as 'glue-lam'. If calculations show a 'glue-lam' column to be incapable of carrying its designed load for a particular supporting function, it is a

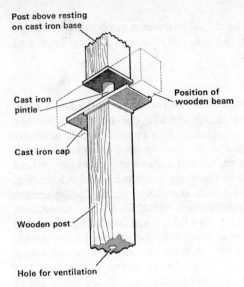

Post above resting
on cast iron base

Cast iron
pintle

Position of
wooden beam

Cast iron cap

Wooden post

Hole for ventilation

Fig. 4.1 Sketch showing the construction of a typical timber post and of the cast-iron cap and pintle used to transmit the load through a floor.

fairly simple matter to satisfy a given fire resistance requirement by adding extra laminations to the originally-designed column. This type of column can be encased with non-combustible insulating material to improve its fire resistance. It has been shown in tests that a 13 mm covering of asbestos insulation board can gain an improvement of 20 minutes' fire resistance. This is achieved by retarding the rate of charring of the laminated timber.

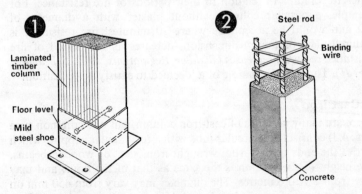

Laminated
timber
column

Floor level

Mild
steel shoe

Steel rod

Binding
wire

Concrete

Fig. 4.2 (1) Sketch showing typical laminated timber column. (2) Sketch showing the construction of a reinforced concrete column

c. Brick

Brick columns are often found in basements supporting beams of wood, cast iron, steel or concrete which in turn carry lengths of continuous brick walling.

d. Stone

Most stone columns are built in one of two ways. In the first a number of single drum-shaped stones are laid one on top of another until the required height is attained. This construction is generally employed for the typical 'classical' columns used ornamentally (and sometimes structurally) in public and commercial buildings. Where classical columns in modern buildings are large and load-bearing, their stone face may conceal steel stanchions inside. In the second method, which is found principally in old churches and cathedrals, the columns are built of a facing of ashlar (i.e. a thin facing of squared stones or thin slabs laid in course with close-fitting joints). Inside may be a mass of rubble or smaller stones loosely bedded and with a much greater proportion of mortar. In the course of centuries this central rubble has often settled, leaving the columns hollow in places so that most of the load is carried by the facing stones.

e. Reinforced concrete

The reinforcing steel bars in structural concrete have been improved over the years and high tensile steel reinforcement often supplemented with a wire mesh cover is now the accepted standard (Fig. 4.2(2)). The fire resistance of a concrete column depends on:

  (i)   the applied load;
  (ii) the strength of the concrete;
  (iii) the size of the column;
  (iv) the method of reinforcement.

The Building Regulations set out the minimum dimension of concrete columns in relation to their periods of fire resistance. For example, a circular column without plaster with a diameter of 150 mm would be acceptable where 30 minutes' fire resistance is required. The minimum dimension increases as the period of fire resistance required increases (*Building Regulations, 1972, Schedule 8, Part II*). This is one example of a 'deemed to satisfy' specification.

f. Cast iron

There are many varieties of cast-iron column, but one common type (Fig. 4.3) consists of a circular tube with a rectangular capping which carries the ends of cast-iron, wrought-iron, steel or wooden beams. The height of the column is the same as that of the floor, and may vary from 2·7 to 6 metres. The diameter may vary from 450 mm on the lowest floor of a large building to 150 mm or less on the top floor of a small building. The bases of the columns on each floor fit into the caps of the columns below, but they are not usually bolted to them. The commonest arrangement is a central spigot and socket joint similar to a drainpipe, but internal wooden plugs are also used.

Solid cast-iron columns were also made having a square or cruciform section.

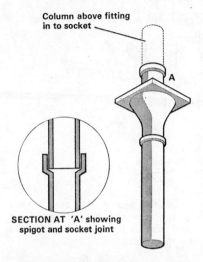

Column above fitting in to socket

A

SECTION AT 'A' showing spigot and socket joint

Fig. 4.3 Sketch showing the construction of a cast-iron column and the method which is used to transmit the load through a floor.

g. Structural steel

A steel column may consist of a single rolled section similar to a steel joist (but usually one of the squarer and heavier standard sections) or it may be built up out of a series of joists, channels, tees, angles and flats riveted together. In the last quarter of the 19th century when the use of steel was developed considerably and it began to be widely employed in building, very complicated columns were built up from smaller sections in this way, but the common practice now is to employ an 'I' section rolled as a single piece and strengthened as necessary by flat plates riveted to the flanges. Steel columns, unlike those of timber or cast iron, are used in long lengths which may run up through several floors, the horizontal joists carrying the various floors being connected to them by brackets bolted or riveted to the side of the column.

Steel is one of the most widely used materials in certain types of building construction, but a disadvantage is its inability to withstand the high temperatures generated in fire conditions. To overcome this, protection must be provided whenever fire resistance is required. This is achieved either by 'solid protection', i.e. the provision of a casing which is bedded to the steel without intervening cavities, or by 'hollow protection', which means that there is a void between the protective material and the steel (Fig. 4.4). All hollow protection to steel columns must be effectively sealed at each floor level.

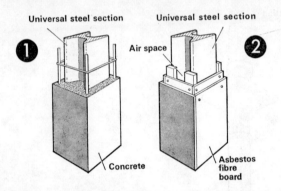

Fig. 4.4 Diagrams showing (1) a universal steel section used as a column with a 'solid protection' fire-resisting casing of reinforced concrete, and (2) a 'hollow protection' encasement of a steel column by means of preformed sections of sprayed asbestos on expanded metal lath.

There are many ways in which this protection can be provided, including concrete or brick encasement, sprayed asbestos and sprayed vermiculite cement for solid protection and plasterboard, asbestos insulating boards, metal lathing covered with cement-lime plaster or sprayed asbestos for hollow protection. The minimum thickness of the various coverings to protect the steel is related to achieve a fire resistance for a specified time.

Heavy steel columns fail less readily than light ones as the thermal capacity (i.e. the ability to absorb heat) of the heavy column is greater for the same temperature rise. Consequently, a light steel column will require as much, and sometimes more, protective covering than a heavy one.

h. Structural aluminium

Although this material is rarely used in practice (it is not likely to be encountered in other than single storey or small two-storey domestic buildings), the fireman should be able to recognise its characteristics when comparing with other structural elements. Structural aluminium alloy columns have a much lower failure temperature than their steel equivalents. Nevertheless, they can be protected by sprayed asbestos to provide solid protection up to 120 minutes' fire resistance, and with plasterboard or metal lathing and plaster (vermiculite-gypsum or perlite-gypsum) to attain the same period of fire resistance in hollow protection. Aluminium has a very high strength to weight ratio which is rapidly lost in fire conditions (see page 13).

j. Fire resistance test of columns

The minimum height of the part exposed in the furnace must be 3 metres and it must be loaded to its design load in actual use in a structure. The specimen is exposed to heat in all directions except when it is to be used in a wall when it is suitably shielded on the unexposed face(s) representing the protection provided by the wall. A column can only be tested for stability and must support its load during the prescribed heating period and also for 24 hours after the end of the heating period. However, should collapse occur during heating, the maximum period of stability is considered to be 80 per cent of the time to collapse. If failure occurs during the reload test, i.e. the 24 hours' support test, the period of stability is considered to be the period that the column has been exposed to heating. It will be seen, therefore, that the heating period must be terminated by estimating the endurance of the column under test for the reload test to be realised. In this way, the performance of every column tested is graded by quoting the actual time to failure in minutes, or the termination of the test within a prescribed time.

2 Beams

The primary function of a structural beam is to support an applied load. A simple beam (Fig. 4.5(1)) is one of short span supported at each end. A continuous beam (Fig. 4.5(2)) is one used in longer spans and supported by a series of columns. In this way greater loads can be carried than by using a series of simple beams.

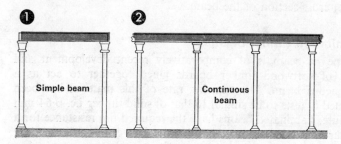

Simple beam

Continuous beam

Fig. 4.5 Diagram showing two types of beam. (1) a simple beam, (2) a continuous beam.

When a load is applied to a beam, it bends slightly (deflects), the upper section being compressed and the lower section tending to stretch (put under tensile stress). This deformation is shown diagrammatically in Fig. 4.6, the amount of deflection being exaggerated for the sake of clarity.

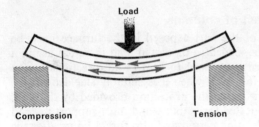

Fig. 4.6 Diagram showing the effect of deflection on a beam. The curvature shown is greatly exaggerated.

a. Timber beams

Except in dwelling houses, timber is not commonly used in structural framing. However as stated previously under 'columns', it will still be found in the older industrial buildings. Balsa is not used structurally and western red cedar is seldom so used; apart from these species, the charring rate of timber is generally accepted as 0·64 mm per minute, although some, e.g. the very dense timbers such as greenheart, jarrah and teak char at about 0·5 mm per minute. When beams or columns are subjected to fire the uncharred core is not materially affected or significantly reduced in strength so that there is no risk of premature failure due to bending. As the fire endurance of timber members can be assessed, the building designer will establish the cross-section of the member for a particular situation according to the fire resistance requirement by calculating the final (after fire) section measurement, and will build up to the actual (pre-fire) cross-section of the beam.

b. Laminated timber beams

This type of beam is of comparatively recent development and consists of softwood timber boards glued together to act as a homogeneous beam. The charring rate of this material has been established in tests to be similar to that of solid timber i.e. 0·64 mm per minute. Laminated beams have the required fire resistance for a particular use designed into them, i.e. the greater the cross section, the longer the period of fire resistance. They can be manufactured to almost any shape.

c. Stone beams

Stone possesses very little strength in tension and is used only for very short spans, such as lintels over openings in walls.

d. Reinforced concrete

To compensate for its lack of tensile strength, concrete is reinforced with high tensile steel rods. Because, as has already been mentioned, the tensile stresses occur in the lower section of a beam, the reinforcing bars are therefore positioned close to the bottom edge. This type of beam is inherently non-combustible. Its fire resistance is dependent upon the cross-sectional area of the beam and the amount of concrete cover provided for the reinforcing bars.

e. Pre-stressed concrete

It has been stated that steel reinforcement is introduced into concrete to withstand the tensile stresses when a load is applied. In effect, this means that the concrete, which resists the compression stresses, and the steel act independently of each other.

Pre-stressing (or pre-compression) introduces stresses which neutralise possible tensile stresses and the whole element, concrete and tendons, acts as one material (Plate 9). By this means advantage is taken of the high grade steels and concrete now available to create longer spans with smaller sizes of beams which in turn effects an economy in supporting columns and foundations.

High tensile steel wires are stretched and kept in a state of tension (see page 10) so that the concrete in the 'tensile zone' is actually in compression. The subsequent external loading merely reduces the amount of pre-compressive stress and only compression exists in all stages of loading, i.e. any would-be tensile stress is neutralised. Fig. 4.7 illustrates this principle and if this is studied with Fig. 4.8

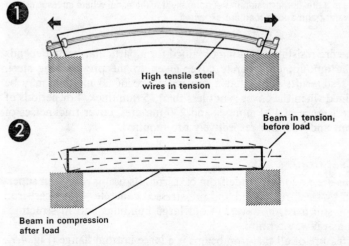

High tensile steel wires in tension

Beam in tension, before load

Beam in compression after load

Fig. 4 7 Diagram showing pre-stressing of concrete beams. (1) Pre-compression induced in the 'fibres' where under working load tensile stresses would be expected. (2) When the load is applied, there remains in the normally 'tensile zone' sufficient compressive stress to neutralise the tensile stresses of the applied load.

the reader will easily obtain an appreciation of the principle involved.

An analogy which might be helpful is that of lifting a number of books from a shelf. If the books are grasped at the top, i.e. compressed from the top, (Fig. 4.8) the books will collapse. This is because by increasing the compression at the top of the 'beam', tensile stresses are also increased at the bottom. When the bottom of the books are compressed, compressive stresses have been induced where tensile stresses are normally expected.

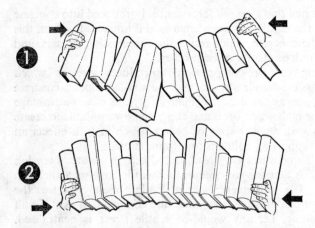

Fig. 4.8 Effect of compression on a row of books. (1) Pressure exerted near the top: the books will collapse. (2) Pressure exerted in the lower section results in a pre-compression in the normally 'tensile zone' where stresses due to self-weight and added load are expected.

The fire resistance grading obtained for a particular beam depends on the amount of concrete cover given to the pre-stressing steel. Fire test results show that a fire resistance of 60 minutes may be obtained when the cover is not less than 45 mm thick. For periods of fire resistance of 120 minutes and 240 minutes, cover thicknesses of 63 mm and 100 mm respectively are required.

f. Cast iron

Beams are no longer made from cast iron, its use having been superseded by steel, reinforced and pre-stressed concrete. Many cast-iron beams still exist, however, in old large buildings and in structures such as railway termini.

A feature of all cast-iron beams is a large bottom flange (Fig. 4.9), the top flange being much smaller, or it may be omitted entirely, resulting in an inverted 'T' beam. Stiffeners are cast on the web and the ends are shaped to fit the head of the cast-iron column to which they are bolted.

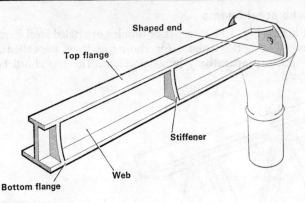

Fig. 4.9 A typical cast-iron beam.

g. Steel

Beams of structural steel are usually referred to by the function they are required to perform, e.g. main beam, tie beam, joist, etc. (see Table 3, page 39). In an H-section beam much of the strength of the material in the central part is wasted so that by utilising the properties of the steel it is possible to reduce very considerably this central part or web as it is called. In such a beam, the top flange carries all the compression and the bottom all the tension. Since the strength of steel is the same in both compression and tension, the flanges of a steel beam are equal. Steel beams (Fig. 4.10) are now most common in the form of a rolled 'I' section of universal beam with, if necessary, extra flats riveted to the top and bottom flanges to give additional strength.

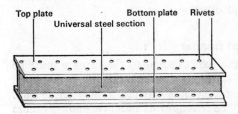

Fig. 4.10 Typical universal steel section with flanges and plates constituting a compound beam.

So far as fire resistance is concerned, the same remarks apply to steel beams as were made about columns, and solid or hollow protection is afforded where fire resistance is required.

h. Open-web steel beams

This type of beam (Fig. 4.11) consists of tubular or angled steel bars welded to top and bottom plates (or chords as they are called), making the beam comparatively light in weight. The top chord is

Fig. 4.11 A typical open-web steel beam.

often provided with a timber fillet to facilitate nailing on fascia boards or other external covering. They are extensively used in single and two-storey industrial and storage buildings.

Another example of an open-web beam is called the 'Castella' beam (Fig. 4.12), which is a beam that has been cut along a castellated line and then welded together again. This increases the depth of the original beam one and a half times, and reduces the deflection under load. The openings in the web of these systems are often used to house electrical and other services.

j. Fire resistance test of beams

The minimum length for the part exposed to the furnace must be 4 metres and the loading is calculated for the particular span related to its design load. The test specimen is exposed to heat on its sides and soffit. A beam can only be tested for its stability. Failure occurs when the deflection of the beam exceeds its length (span) divided by 30.

k. Fire resistance test for suspended ceilings protecting steel beams

A test has been established for suspended ceilings to indicate their ability to protect steel beams against fire, other than by individual encasement, so that such assemblies can be classified for fire resistance. Measurements are taken during this test to assess the contribution the ceiling makes to the fire resistance of the floor supported by the beams.

Solid rolled steel or open-web beams are used to support the ceiling, the minimum specimen size being 2.5 by 4 metres. The beams are covered with a concrete floor 130 mm thick. The whole assembly is installed for testing as it would be in service including light fittings, recesses for light fittings and openings for ducting whenever these factors are appropriate. The specimen ceiling is judged on its ability to protect the beams to their maximum design stresses. The limit of effective protection is deemed to have occurred when:

(i) one or more tiles or panels become dislodged, or
(ii) with a loaded specimen, the beams are unable to support the load, or the temperature of any beam exceeds a mean value of 550°C or a maximum of 650°C, or if the maximum deflection is in excess of the span of the floor divided by 30, or
(iii) with an unloaded specimen, the temperature of any beam at any measuring point exceeds 400°C.

This type of ceiling is often referred to as a 'membrane ceiling'.

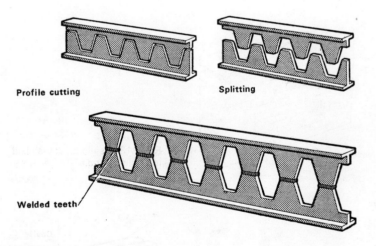

Profile cutting   **Splitting**

Welded teeth

Fig. 4.12 Example of an open-web 'Castella' beam showing how the original beam is cut and rewelded to reduce the deflection under load.

3 Walls (load-bearing)

In modern methods of construction, walls which comprise elements of structure are named according to the function they perform, i.e.

external wall, compartment wall, separating wall and load-bearing wall. Firemen do not only deal with modern construction and must know about wall constructions of all types, some of which would not be acceptable in modern building practice. In the following paragraphs the principal types of load-bearing wall construction are shown.

a. Solid brick

The commonest type of load-bearing wall, and one which is also widely used as a non-load-bearing panel wall in a framed building, is that made of brick. The nominal size of a brick, at least in the south of England, is 228 by 114 by 76 mm, and the thickness of a brick wall is measured in multiples of a half brick, (i.e. 114 mm). Thus a 'brick and a half wall' as shown in Fig. 4.13 is 342 mm, and a 'half brick wall' is 114 mm thick. The bricks are bedded in mortar which may consist of a mixture of lime and sand with water (lime mortar) or a lime mortar to which has been added a proportion of cement (lime cement mortar or 'compo') or of a mortar consisting of cement, sand and water. Lime mortar is relatively soft and may be protected on the outside of the building by 'pointing' the joints in a stronger mortar.

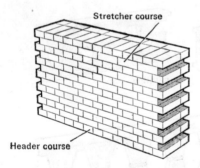

Stretcher course

Header course

Fig. 4.13 A solid brick wall laid in English bond.

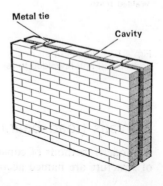

Metal tie

Cavity

Fig. 4.14 A brick cavity wall, showing the metal ties and stretcher bond with, at the ends, snap headers.

Bricks are arranged in a wall so that the vertical joints of one layer or 'course' of bricks do not coincide with the joints of the course below. This is known as 'bonding' and a number of different arrangements or 'bonds' are in general use; that shown in Fig. 4.13 is the strongest type and the most usual in this country for thick walls, and is known appropriately as 'English bond'. The cavity wall construction (Fig. 4.14) described in par. (b) below is laid in 'stretcher bond' (i.e. bricks laid lengthways) with snap headers (i.e. bricks cut in half and laid with their ends on the face of the wall) to give the necessary bond.

b. Cavity brick

Cavity walls are used mainly as external walls in buildings particularly exposed to weather. The object of the cavity is to prevent rain penetrating to the inside face of the wall. The usual type of cavity wall found in domestic buildings (Fig. 4.14) consists of two half-brick walls held together by metal ties and separated by a 50 mm cavity. Sometimes the internal wall is only 76 mm thick in modern buildings and is built either of bricks laid on edge or of concrete slabs. Whatever method is employed, the weight of the upper floors and sometimes of the roof is carried on this internal wall.

The cavity may or may not be ventilated to the outside air by air bricks at the top and bottom. In modern building practice, the cavity is sometimes filled with an inert material giving additional thermal insulation to the building.

c. Solid brick faced with stone

This type of construction (Fig. 4.15) is used as a cheaper substitute for a solid stone wall in commercial and public buildings, and may be either load-bearing or a panel wall in a framed building. The

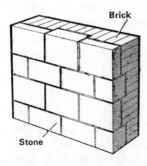

Fig. 4.15 A solid brick wall faced with stone.

stone blocks are built up at the same time as the brickwork and are bonded to it. For decorative treatment, particularly inside large buildings, brick or other walls may be found to which thin slabs of natural or artificial stone are fixed by metal cramps (Fig. 4.16) or even (for internal decoration) by plaster.

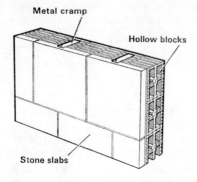

Fig. 4.16 A hollow block wall faced with thin stone slabs.

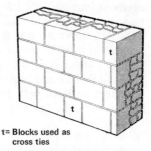

Fig. 4.17 A solid stone wall showing the method of strengthening by means of occasional ties.

t= Blocks used as cross ties

d. Solid stone

A stone wall is commonly thicker than a corresponding brick wall for it is rarely less than 305 mm thick. Many different types of bonding or arrangement of stones are used, depending on local tradition and on the size and workability of the stones as they are quarried. One of the commonest arrangements is some variety of the type illustrated in Fig. 4.17. In this example the outside face is of large stones squared and fitted together with thin joints. A number of these facing stones are run through the thickness of the wall as strengthening ties. The inside face of the wall, where appearance is unimportant, consists of a mixture of medium and large stones more roughly fitted together.

e. Timber framed

Timber in external walls has been used for farm buildings for many years, both for the framework and for cladding. In recent times its use has been widely adopted for houses both for 'cross wall' types (brick or block separating walls with light framing to form the front

54

and rear elevations), and the increasingly found completely timber-framed house.

Modern temporary buildings, such as school class rooms, building site offices, and commercial offices, frequently employ timber external walls. The thermal insulation requirements of external of walls dwellings can often result indirectly in improved fire resistance due to the high temperature resistance of the rock wools commonly incorporated. This does not apply where plastics type insulations are used.

There are many variations of the timber-framed load-bearing wall, a type of construction which has developed through the centuries. The half-timbered house probably represents the best example. In this type the 'skeleton' of the building is composed of heavy timber members, and to keep out the weather the spaces between the members are filled in with brickwork often laid in a decorative manner. Brickwork filled in between timbers is termed 'nogging'. Lighter-framed walls, such as are used for the internal divisions of houses, which nevertheless often carry some load, are composed of vertical members termed 'studs', braced as necessary to give them rigidity. To form the 'partition' these studs are covered on infilled with a variety of materials. Modern timber stud walls clad with plasterboard or asbestos insulation board can be constructed to be capable of resisting the effects of fire for an hour or even more (to meet the Building Regulations), and the thicknesses and type of lining board used will usually determine the resistance obtainable.

A brick-nogged partition is a wooden stud partition in which the spaces between the wooden studs are filled in with bricks. The thickness of the brick is 114 mm if the bricks are laid normally, or 76 mm if they are laid on edge as shown in Fig. 4.18. Wooden spacers known as nogging pieces are used to strengthen the partition longitudinally.

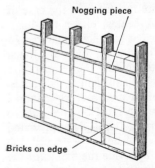

Fig. 4.18 A brick-nogged wall.

Another type of partition, common in Scotland, consists of a half-brick wall tied together every six or seven courses with a horizontal wood strip 25 mm thick running the full thickness of the wall and, if possible, its full length also.

Early walls (Fig. 4.19) had a layer of reeds affixed on either face by laths to the studs. These reeds were then plastered over with mud or lime plaster to give a 'wattle-and-daub' wall (Plate 10). The space between the two layers was often filled in with mud or rough plaster. This type of wall is now obsolete but may be found in some old buildings, particularly those of half-timbered construction. In due course, layers of reeds were replaced by wooden laths nailed direct on to the studding.

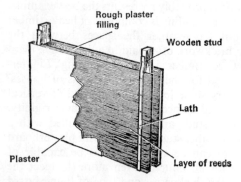

Fig. 4.19 A wattle-and-daub wall.

f. Fire resistance of timber-framed walls

Timber-framed walls whether load-bearing or not can be designed to provide substantial fire resistance. It will be the residual section of the studs which will largely dictate the fire resistance in the case of load-bearing walls. As with columns or beams, either the load-bearing members must incorporate sufficient sacrificial material or they must be adequately protected. Partitioning or walls must resist the passage of flames in addition to limiting the temperature rise on the non-fire side. This then calls for sufficient resistance to fire from the two linings in combination. It must not be assumed however that each side of a framed partition must be able only to resist the fire for half of the required period. It will be appreciated that the earlier in a fire the lining on the fire side is destroyed, the sooner will the fire attack the studs which provide the fixing for the farther lining. If sound insulation (in addition to fire resistance) is a requirement, then the linings may be substantial and/or, the cavities will incorporate a sound absorbent. A fire resistant sound absorbent can be fitted so as to provide some protection to the studs, so prolonging their life during a fire; as well as that of the farther lining.

g. Behaviour of load-bearing walls in a fire

The stability of a brick or stone wall depends, amongst other things, upon its thickness in relation to its height, on proper bonding (in particular on the use of sufficient headers to tie the wall together), to some extent on its age, and on any horizontal pushing or levering effect which may be exerted upon it. In a stone wall it also depends on the proportion of smaller stones which have been used and the skill with which they have been fitted together. The fewer the number of joints and the thinner they are, the greater the strength of a stone wall.

A brick or stone wall, though capable of supporting a considerable vertical load, can only withstand a comparatively small sideways or lateral pressure, and, for stability, the loading of a wall must be centred within the middle third (Fig. 4.20). Provision is usually made in the design of a structure to withstand any normal lateral pressure either by making the walls themselves thick enough for the purpose, or by the erection of transverse walls or buttresses, but abnormal

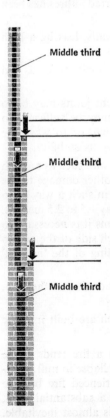

Middle third

Middle third

Middle third

Fig. 4.20 Diagram (not to scale) showing how the load on a wall or column must be concentrated within the middle third.

57

conditions for which no provision has been made, may be brought about at a fire. The expansion of steel joists may exert lateral pressure upon the load-bearing walls into which they enter and expansion or other movement of the contents of the building may have a similar effect. Both of these causes have been known to bring about the collapse of substantial brick walls.

A further frequent cause of collapse is uneven expansion. The heat conductivity of brick or stone is very low, and it takes some time for heat to penetrate from one side of a wall to the other. The temperature of the surface of a brick wall in contact with a fire may, in consequence, be considerably higher than that of the farther surface and differences of as much as 500°C have been recorded in walls only one brick thick (i.e. 228 mm). Since a rise in temperature causes expansion, it is obvious that if one surface of the wall is exposed to heat and expands whilst the other remains cool, the effect will be to bend the wall and throw it out of vertical, and, in extreme cases, to cause its collapse.

In general the collapse of walls which has occurred at fires has been due to:

(i) The burning away of the floors and cross walls, leaving a high wall with no side support.

(ii) Expansion of beams built into the wall pushing it outwards and so throwing it out of equilibrium.

(iii) Disintegration of the joints. Lime and cement joints may be so weakened by fire that a jet from a branch may be sufficient to throw the wall off balance and bring it down, or to wash the loose mortar out of the joints and so destroy its stability.

(iv) The collapse of the support at the base of the wall such as an arch or a heavy steel beam. Provided there is no other damage to the wall, however, the bricks or stones may fall in such a way as to leave a natural arch over quite a large span (say 1.5 to 2.5 metres), and thus prevent total collapse. If this happens it is necessary to see that there is ample wall remaining on each side of the gap to support the load above and to resist spreading of the 'natural' arch.

(v) Heating and consequent expansion of the inside face of the wall, throwing the wall outwards.

(vi) The levering action of collapsing joists which are built into the wall.

Experience in the collapse of stone walls in a fire tends to be contradictory. There have been many cases of collapse in mill buildings in the north of England, and many experienced fire brigade officers consider that once a fire has obtained a substantial hold, collapse of some part at least of the structure is almost inevitable. In Scotland, on the other hand, where stone walls are almost universal, hardly any collapses have occurred, and stone walls are generally regarded as safe in almost any circumstances. The reason for this difference in behaviour may be the greater thickness and solidity of construction in Scotland, or, possibly, in the type of stone used. Provided, however, that a stone wall is well built, its fire resistance may be considered as substantially the same as that of a similar thickness of solid brick.

In a fire a solid brick wall faced with stone behaves much the same as a solid brick or stone wall, and there is little danger of the stone facing peeling off. On the other hand, when only a thin stone slab facing is used – often inadequately bonded or fixed to the wall – there is a danger of these slabs coming away from the wall in a fire or as a result of explosion. The wattle-and-daub wall is not fire-resisting, but it has been found in practice to delay the spread of fire and tends to smoulder rather than burn rapidly.

At the beginning of the last century many buildings were built with their walls covered outside with plaster or 'stucco' as a cheap imitation of stonework. In this type of building the ornamental features, such as cornices, balconies, columns, etc. may consist of stucco on wooden laths fixed to a wooden framework. The wood is often extremely dry and the number of small concealed spaces make fire fighting very difficult.

h. Fire tests for walls

Walls are tested by being subjected to gradually increasing heat from a furnace which varies with time according to a standard time-temperature relationship. When it is not possible to test a full-size specimen, the minimum dimensions of the part exposed to the furnace is 2·5 square metres. The loading is that to which the wall or part of the wall would normally be loaded in service. Walls which may be required to resist fire from both directions are tested on the side expected to give the lower fire resistance; should there be any doubts, then tests are made from each side separately.

The fire resistance of a wall is determined by the time in minutes from the start of the test until failure occurs of stability, integrity or insulation. In determining the integrity of a wall, a dry cotton wool pad is held about 25 mm from any crack or other opening which may appear, for 10 seconds. Failure is deemed to have occurred when flame or hot gases pass through the crack and cause the pad to ignite.

4 Floors

In all except single-storey buildings, floors are a principal structural element. The general structural design greatly influences the type of floor used. For example, an office block might be constructed as a steel-framed building or in reinforced concrete. A different type of floor is appropriate in each case, even though performances required in terms of fire resistance, loading, span and sound insulation are identical. In the steel-framed building, the frame is designed to support the floor. It is therefore quicker and more economical for the designer to use precast concrete units and eliminate the necessity to shuttering and wet pouring of concrete. In the reinforced concrete building, the designer can take into account the strength that the floors can add to the structure as a whole. In such a building it is generally found that *in situ* concrete floors are used, being cast simultaneously with the beams. Shuttering and wet pouring is required in this type of construction in any case. Hence there are many and varied types of floor determined by the design of particular buildings.

It is useful to regard floors as composed of three parts: the actual load-bearing members which give the floor its strength, the upper surface or floor finish and the lower surface or ceiling. Sometimes these parts are actually separate and identifiable, sometimes they are combined. For example, in a timber floor in a small house, the load-bearing members are the joists, the surface is the boarding and the ceiling is of plaster. Here, the preponderance of the strength of the combination is provided by the joists, and, while the boarding adds to the rigidity, it is not an essential contributor; the plaster is itself supported by the joists. Compare this with a reinforced concrete floor in which all three parts, ceiling, floor surface and structure may be completely merged; the whole thickness of the concrete slab contributes to the strength of the floor and the upper and lower surfaces provide the floor surface and ceiling. This factor becomes more important when we come to consider membrane or suspended ceilings and compartmentation.

Construction of the more common types of floor is explained in the following paragraphs.

a. Timber floors

Timber floors (and flooring) may be found in all types of building except the upper floors of those used for institutional purposes (i.e. hospitals, old persons' homes, etc.) which have been built since 1966. For many years Building Regulations (previously Building Byelaws) have required upper floors to provide a certain minimum period of fire resistance. This period varies with the size and type of building. Ceiling materials, such as lath and plaster, asbestos fibre board or plasterboard, add considerably to the fire resistance of the timber floor itself. Other factors in the performance in fire of timber floors include:

(i) whether the flooring is plain edged (butted) or tongued and grooved boarding, chipboard or plywood;

(ii) the thickness of the flooring;

(iii) the load-bearing capacity of the joists;

(iv) the contribution made to the fire resistance by the ceiling.

It should be noted that sound insulation requirements often dictate substantial thicknesses of ceiling material which serve the dual purpose of providing additional fire resistance. Many older buildings, particularly factory premises, have no ceiling fixed below an upper floor and therefore the fire resistance may be short.

In studying the construction of the timber floors shown below, it should be noted that where boarding is indicated as the flooring material in the more modern buildings, this could be chipboard or plywood sheets.

b. Timber-joisted floors

The timber-joisted floor (Fig. 4.21) has been generally used for the upper floors of houses of all periods. Butt-jointed or tongued and grooved boarding between about 16 and 32 mm thick is used, laid

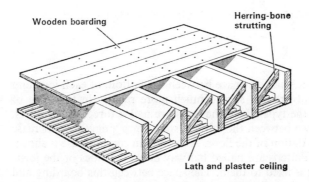

Wooden boarding

Herring-bone strutting

Lath and plaster ceiling

Fig. 4.21 A typical timber-joisted floor as used in domestic houses.

on wooden joists usually not less than 50 mm thick and varying in depth from 127 to 180 mm according to the distance they span. These joists may be prevented from twisting by strutting, of which each unit may be either a solid board or two cross herringbone struts although the nailed boards will often have the same effect. On the underside of the joists is the ceiling, usually of lath and plaster, or in modern work, of building board finished with a thin coat of plaster. It can be seen that there is a space between each pair of joists which is enclosed by the floorboards above and the ceiling below. This space constitutes a hazard because fire can travel in it undetected and, in the case of a hearth fire in particular (see the *Manual, Part 6A: Chapter 1*—Book 11 in the new format), it is often necessary to lift the floorboards at intervals to verify that the fire has not travelled to some other part of the structure through this space.

In Scotland the laths or plasterboard are nailed to small battens called branders which run across the underside of the floor joists (Fig. 4.22). These branders prevent the joists from twisting, and strutting is not therefore used. Since the laths are held away from the

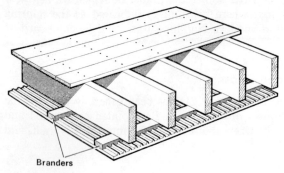

Branders

Fig. 4.22 Method of securing the ceiling laths to branders, sometimes used in Scotland.

joists there is a small air space between the bottom of each joist and the ceiling and fire can spread much more rapidly in this type of floor then in the type where the laths are nailed direct to the joists.

The air space between the joists is sometimes 'pugged' to increase the sound insulation of the floor. A method in common use is shown in Fig. 4.23. Battens are nailed halfway down the sides of the joists and boarding is fixed to them. The space between this boarding and the underside of the floorboards is filled with ashes or other packing (which may sometimes be of a flammable nature, such as sawdust or shavings) and finished off with a mixture of lime and sand. The effect of pugging is, in general, to increase to a reasonable extent the fire resistance of the floor.

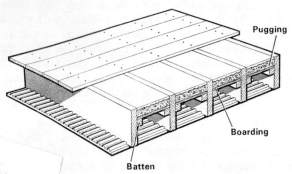

Pugging

Boarding

Batten

Section of a floor cut away to show pugging.

The way in which the joists are supported on the walls is of importance to the fireman, for several methods are employed. In old work, the joists are simply built into the wall (Fig. 4.24(1)) and there is a risk that the collapse of the joists in a fire will lever the wall off its balance. A commoner method is the provision of a wooden wall plate on to which the ends of the joists are nailed (Fig. 4.24(2)). This wall plate, if built into the wall, tends to weaken it. Another method

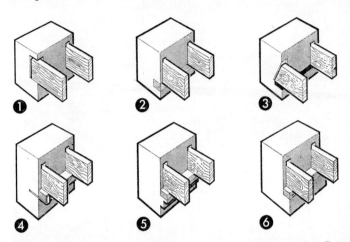

Fig. 4.24 Sketches showing various arrangements for supporting floor joists: (1) joist with square end in pocket; (2) joist carried on wooden wall plate; (3) joist with splayed end in pocket; (4) joist carried on wooden wall plate carried on bracket; (5) joist carried on wooden wall plate on corbelled brickwork; (6) joist carried on wooden wall plate on a ledge formed by reducing the thickness of the wall.

sometimes encountered is to build in a wrought steel wall plate (Fig. 4.24(3)). Whichever system is adopted the wall is liable to be levered off its balance by collapsing joists unless the joist pockets are big enough to allow the joists to fall freely.

Of the more satisfactory methods employed (considered from the point of view of fire risk) one is to support the wall plate on wrought-iron brackets built into the wall (Fig. 4.24(4)) a second is to corbel the brickwork out to form a ledge for the wooden wall plate (Fig. 4.24(5)), whilst a third is to reduce the thickness of the wall by 114 mm at each floor level and to rest the wall plate on the resulting ledge (Fig. 4.24(6)). A further method sometimes used is to splay the end of the joist as shown in Fig. 4.24(3).

c. Brick arches on cast-iron beams

In this type of floor cast-iron, or sometimes steel, beams are carried on a series of columns and the space between the beams is filled with shallow brick arches. The parts of the arch (Fig. 4.25) nearest the beam are built of bricks on end, and the centre of bricks on edge. The resulting uneven top surface is levelled off with weak concrete 'pugging'. Wooden boarding is laid immediately over the concrete by nailing it to cast-in wooden strips. Alternative floor coverings which are found in 228 mm square floor tiles and stone flags similar to those used for pavements. This type of floor was in common use for mills and warehouses up to about 1890.

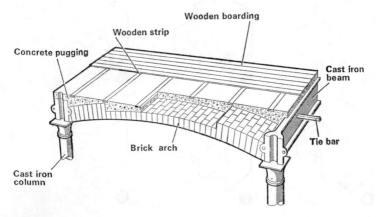

Fig. 4.25 A brick arched floor carried on cast-iron beams and columns.

d. Steel 'filler' joists and mass concrete

There are many varieties of this type of floor, but the principle universally employed is to divide up the area to be filled in by steel joists into units sufficiently small to be spanned by mass (i.e. un-reinforced) concrete. Most of these floors were built between about 1885 and 1910 before reinforced concrete and hollow tile floors became common. Two floors are illustrated in Figs. 4.26 and 4.27. In the first (Fig. 4.26) for example, light steel joists 101 by 44 mm are placed 300 mm apart and the space between and above filled in with 200 mm of concrete. The top is finished off smooth and may be boarded, tiled, etc. as required, whilst the underside is usually plas-tered. This type of floor has a very good fire record especially where it is supported on substantial brick walls.

In the second type (Fig. 4.27) the steel joists are heavier and spaced more widely apart, whilst the concrete is arched up from the bottom flange of the joist to reduce the weight of the floor. The thickness of ~~crete at the centre of the slabs may be as little as 76 to 101 mm ~~re there is a danger of the slabs cracking away from the the second type, and sometimes also in the first type, the

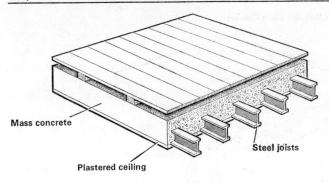

Mass concrete

Plastered ceiling

Steel joists

Fig. 4.26 Mass concrete and steel filler joist floor.

lower flange of the steel joist is completely unprotected and is exposed to the full heat of any fire which may occur in the space below it.

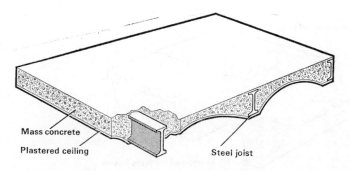

Mass concrete

Plastered ceiling

Steel joist

Fig. 4.27 Steel filler joist with arched construction mass concrete floor.

e. Solid reinforced concrete

In this type of floor (Fig. 4.28), the steel rods which take the tension are situated in the lower part of the slab and are protected by a thin layer of concrete. In 'cross-reinforced' floors the rods run both ways to form a grid. The floor covering is arranged to suit the occupancy of the building. Whilst these floors are rarely less than 127 mm in thickness, a thin floor (i.e. 76 or 101 mm thick) as might be used for very small spaces with thin rods (13 mm) thinly protected by concrete may have a poor fire resistance.

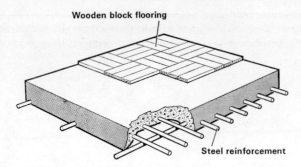

Fig. 4.28 Solid slab reinforced concrete floor.

f. Reinforced concrete rib

This is a modification of the solid slab floor to give a lighter form of reinforced concrete construction. The area to be covered is divided up by a series of reinforced concrete beams (Fig. 4.29) spaced from 450 to 610 mm apart which project into the room below, the spaces

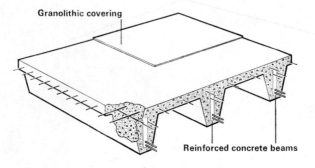

Fig. 4.29 Reinforced concrete rib and panel floor.

between the beams being spanned with reinforced concrete slabs which are structurally continuous with the beams. The thickness of the concrete panels is less than that of a concrete floor without ribs, and may be as little as 50 mm to 76 mm. The fire resistance of this type of floor is somewhat inferior to that of the heavier reinforced concrete floor largely because of its reduced thickness.

⌐re-stressed concrete

ϳe of floor pre-stressed solid concrete planks serve as
⸝ formwork instead of the usual timber shuttering, and so

form an integral part of a structural concrete floor (Plates 11 and 12). The planks are laid side by side (Fig. 4.30) and are then covered with concrete which bonds to the planks and acts with them. In effect, therefore, the finished floor is a solid slab with pre-stressed reinforcement.

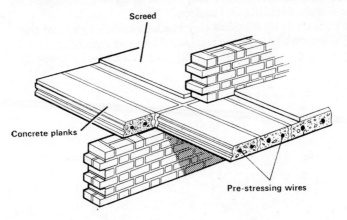

Fig. 4.30 Solid pre-stressed plank type of concrete floor.

Pre-stressed hollow concrete planks are also used (Fig. 4.31). They range in depth from 150 to 400 mm and are made up to 14 metres in length. They are laid in similar fashion to the solid pre-stressed planks, but in addition tie bars are laid between the lengthways planks.

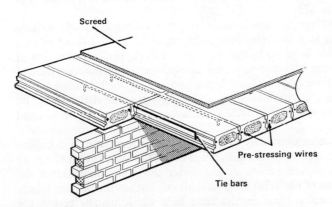

Fig. 4.31 Pre-stressed hollow plank type of concrete floor.

h. Hollow tile

Where, as in office buildings, floor loadings are not substantial, hollow tile floors are more widely used than those of solid reinforced concrete, the former being lighter in weight for an equal strength, which has economic advantages at low loadings. A large number of different types are in common use, but, with a few exceptions, they can be classified under two headings.

One consists of light hollow clay blocks, similar in size and shape to clay partition blocks, set in reinforced concrete and covered on the top by a layer of concrete (Fig 4.32). The other type of lightweight

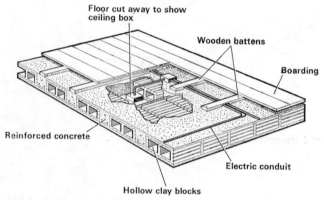

Fig. 4.32 Hollow block and reinforced concrete floor.

floor (Fig. 4.33) consists of a series of hollow precast-concrete beams laid close together and with their ends resting on steel joists. The joints between the beams are filled in with a thin concrete made from sand and cement.

Hollow clay tiles and hollow concrete beams are liable to lose their lower face in a fire, thus reducing their fire resistance to that which would be given by the thickness of the upper face plus that of any concrete or other covering above. As many modern framed buildings have hollow tile or beam floors, it is worth bearing this in mind. There is, unfortunately, no simple way of determining by observation which is a hollow tile floor and which is one of solid concrete.

In all but exceptionally fierce fires, the performance of a hollow tile floor in regard to fire resistance is about the same as that of a solid reinforced concrete floor. A fire under the floor often causes the face of the hollow tile to spall off, but, as the bottom face is ally essential, the floor as a whole usually resists the ire.

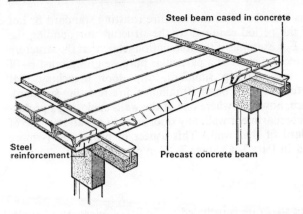

Fig. 4.33 Hollow concrete beam and reinforced concrete floor.

j. Fire tests for floors

The specimen submitted for test in accordance with BS 476, Part 8, must be at least 2.5 metres wide with a 4 metres span. Where a ceiling treatment or suspended ceiling is intended to contribute to the fire resistance of the floor, the ceiling is incorporated and put under test with the floor. No account is taken of a purely decorative suspended ceiling. The load applied is that which the floor is designed to carry at normal temperatures. The specimen floor is exposed to heat from the underside and must satisfy the criteria for stability, integrity and insulation. Another factor is also observed in the case of a floor, known as 'deflection'; this is mentioned in relation to beams in Section 2(k)(ii) on page 51.

5 Structure enclosing a protected shaft

A shaft within a building, whether it be horizontal or vertical, is a potential source of weakness by which a fire can spread unless adequate precautions are taken. A protected shaft is defined in the Building Regulations as being a stairway, lift, escalator, chute, duct or other shaft which enables persons, things or air to pass between different compartments, and which complies with the various rules for different types of occupancy set out in the Regulations for its protection. In general terms the structure enclosing a protected vertical shaft must be so constructed to ensure that fire from an adjacent space cannot enter the shaft. The weakness is in the access to the shaft by means of doors to staircases and lift enclosures. These access doors must therefore be fire resisting. Depending on the occupancy this must be to 30 minutes fire resisting standard or not less than half the period required by the structure surrounding the door opening. For example, if the Regulations state that the structure enclosing a protected shaft of a particular purpose group must be of 120 minutes' fire resisting standard, any door breaching that structural protection must be of 60 minutes' fire resisting standard. (In any instance, however, where one of the walls enclosing a protected shaft is a compartment wall, any door in such a wall must be of the full standard of that wall.) This aspect of protection is more fully explained in Part 3, Chapter 7, 'Compartmentation'.

6 Galleries

This element of structure is included in the list of 'elements of structure' in the Building Regulations, but is not defined. It can be described as a raised floor or balcony over part of the area of a full span floor. In most cases a gallery will not perform any supporting function in a building, but will more likely itself be supported. As all elements of structure are required to have a specified period of fire resistance according to the purpose group (and other factors) of the building, it would be illogical to exclude a gallery from this requirement, bearing in mind the test criteria for collapse, passage of flame and insulation.

Chapter 5
Other elements of structure

1 Foundations

The fireman is not particularly concerned with foundations from a fire-fighting point of view, but even an elementary study of building construction requires some understanding of the function of foundations. Foundations must sustain and transmit all the loads likely to arise from a building to the supporting ground, and the form they take will differ according to the type of construction and the nature of the ground upon which the building is to be erected (Fig. 5.1).

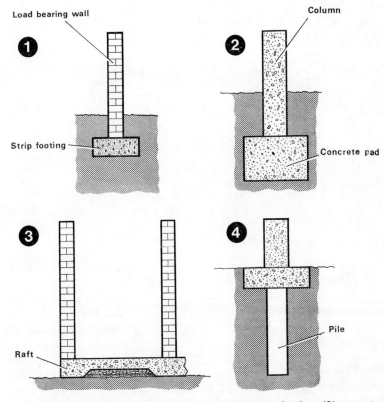

Fig. 5.1 Examples of various types of foundation. (1) strip footing; (2) concrete pad; (3) raft; (4) pile.

A load-bearing wall will normally have a continuous strip footing, whilst steel and reinforced concrete frame construction will normally carry the loads through the columns and through separate mass or reinforced concrete pads or bases beneath each column. When the load carried by each column is high, independent bases would need to be very large, so, in these cases, designers usually combine them into one large raft. If the ground near the surface is soft, but lower down beneath the upper layer is another of adequate strength to carry the applied load, piles are driven or bored to carry the loads. In some cases, piles gain their strength by means of the friction between the sides of the pile and the ground surrounding them.

2 Roofs

A roof is the structure which surmounts a building to keep out the weather, and may be flat, pitched or curved.

a. Flat roofs

The simplest type of roof is the flat roof. The structural part of a flat roof is similar in construction to a floor, and may consist of wooden joists and boarding (Fig. 5.2), concrete (Fig. 5.3), hollow

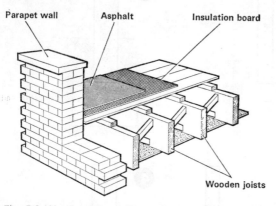

Parapet wall   Asphalt   Insulation board

Wooden joists

Fig. 5.2 Wooden-joisted flat roof with parapet. For simplicity details of the damp course have been omitted from the parapet wall.

tiles, or any other type of floor construction. Above this is fixed some kind of waterproof layer, such as asphalt, bitumen impregnated roofing felt and metal sheeting.

b. Pitched roofs

A common type of roof is the pitched roof. By its use (except in large and expensive buildings), it is possible to obtain greater spans than with a simple beam such as a joist.

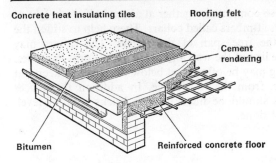

Concrete heat insulating tiles   Roofing felt

Cement
rendering

Bitumen   Reinforced concrete floor

Fig. 5.3 Concrete flat roof without parapet.

(1) Close-coupled roofs

The simplest and most common form of pitched roof is called a
close-coupled roof (Fig. 5.4). Timber rafters, about 300 mm apart,
run from a ridge board to a wall plate on the top of the external wall

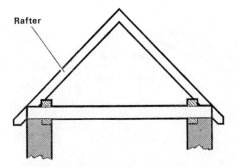

Rafter

Fig. 5.4 The simplest form of pitched roof construction – the close-coupled
roof and one which is generally used for the ordinary small traditional type of
dwelling house.

at eaves level. These rafters carry the sloping roof which can be of
various materials (described below). Where rafters are longer than
about 2 metres, they require support in the middle (Fig. 5.5). This is
done by a timber, called a purlin, which supports the centres of all
the rafters, and on long spans is itself supported by timber struts
placed at intervals on the tops of the internal walls. On very large
close-coupled roofs there may be two purlins under each slope.

The ceiling joists are nailed to the wallplate and to the rafters, so
that the whole construction forms a series of triangles which resist
any tendency for the roof to spread outwards. Occasionally the two

73

sets of rafters are also connected together at about half the height of the roof by transverse timbers called collars. These help to stiffen the roof by reducing the free span of the rafters. The rafters may continue beyond the line of the wall and overhang to form the eaves. Horizontal boarding may be often used below the eaves to keep out draughts, birds, etc. from the roof space. In addition the spaces between the rafters should be filled in with bricks to roof level, but often this is not done.

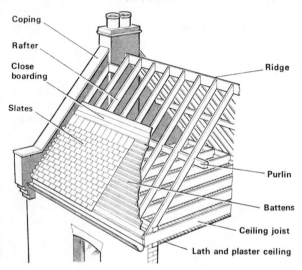

Fig. 5.5 Sketch showing the more important features of the form of roof construction often used in domestic dwellings.

This type of construction is mostly used in houses as well as for great numbers of other small buildings; there are several variations. For instance, the ceiling joists may be set up above the level of the top of the walls so that the rafters form part of the ceiling in the room below. This is known as a 'camp roof'. Again, it may be found that rooms have been formed in the roof space if it is high enough, by means of vertical timber framing (Fig. 5.6), the whole being lined with lath and plaster, or some form of wallboard. The framing thus forms vertical walls to the rooms; there is some sloping ceiling on the underside of the rafters and a horizontal portion on the underside of the collars.

In the construction of timber roofs, connector or connection joints are used. 'Joist hangers', 'bolts', 'framing anchors' and 'steel timber connectors' are a few of the devices which are replacing established joinery techniques.

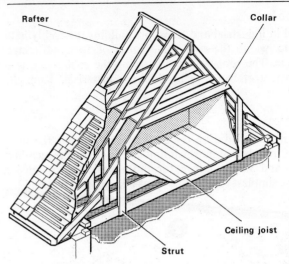

Fig. 5.6 Sketch showing how part of the roof void may be utilised to form a room.

(2) Mansard roofs

A mansard roof is a special kind of pitched roof. Instead of the roof running up at a constant angle from eaves to ridge, there are two angles – a very steep pitch (Fig. 5.7(1)) running from the eaves to room height, and a flatter pitch (2) above. The object of this is to

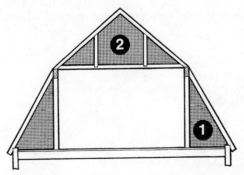

Fig. 5.7 Diagram showing the voids left in mansard roof construction: (1) is the void left by the steep pitch and (2) the void left by the flatter pitch.

enable a room to be placed inside the roof space which, in effect, becomes an additional storey. The name Mansard is that of the French architect (1598–1666) who first used this design.

c. Trussed roofs

Trussing is used in industrial and transport building, assembly halls and hangers, etc. where the roof spans areas of 10 to 60 metres between supports. The roof structure carrying the roof covering is erected in a variety of forms using different materials. Examples are given below:

(1) Timber trusses

In buildings constructed during the 19th century, by far the most common type of truss is that in which timber is used for the members in compression and wrought iron for those subjected to tension (Fig. 5.8(1)). The simplest form is known as a king post truss and has

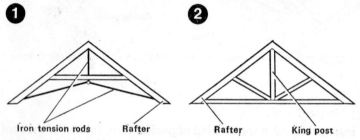

1   **2**

Iron tension rods   Rafter   Rafter   King post

Fig. 5.8 (1) A composite truss with timber compression members and wrought iron tension rods. (2) A king post truss.

a single vertical member placed centrally (Fig. 5.8(2)). In the queen post truss (Fig. 5.9) – the type most commonly encountered – there

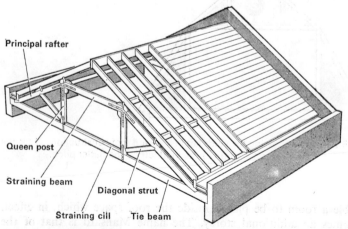

Principal rafter

Queen post

Straining beam

Diagonal strut

Straining cill   Tie beam

Fig. 5.9 A roof carried on queen post trusses.

are two vertical ties or queen posts, which are strutted apart at their heads by a horizontal beam called a straining beam, and at their feet by a straining cill. The principal rafters span between the heads of the queen posts and the ends of the tie beam, and are supported by diagonal struts. All these wooden members are of heavy section. It is very common to find that the space between the two queen posts has either been used for storage or accommodation access gangways, shafting or conveyor belts (Plate 13).

A common type of wooden truss which gives a curved roof, is the 'Belfast' (Fig. 5.10). It is very simple to construct; it can cover large spans and low-grade timber of small sizes can be employed. It was first developed on a large scale during World War I for aircraft hangars and war factories. It is now used extensively on timber storage sheds and similar buildings. It commonly has a decking of boarding which is covered with bituminous felt; occasionally corrugated iron is used. A Belfast roof can be distinguished from the outside by its characteristic curved shape and from the inside by the lattice-like design of the timber of which it is constructed.

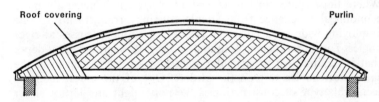

Roof covering   Purlin

Fig. 5.10 Sketch showing how a timber truss for a Belfast roof is made up.

(2) Laminated timber trussing

The development of new efficient waterproof glues has made possible the use of laminated arches and trusses. The strength of timber is variable but, by laminating it in small sections, the local weaknesses of timber can be overcome; this reduces the risk of faults occurring throughout the full thickness of the timber. Light framework can be built requiring little maintenance, and spans up to 45 metres can be covered using 'bowstring' trusses, 'girder' trusses and laminated arches.

(3) Cast iron trussing

Cast-iron trusses in one, two or more sections were in use in the last century in factories and warehouses. A Victorian example of a north light truss cast in one piece is shown in Fig. 5.11, whilst another example is shown in Plate 14.

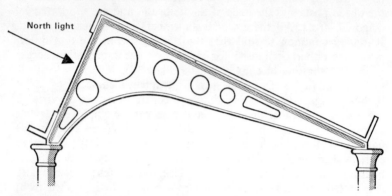

Fig. 5.11 Sketch showing an example of a north light truss case in one piece.

(4) Steel lattice girders

Where floor spans start to exceed 15 metres, it is generally more economical to change from simple trussing arrangements to one employing wide span lattice girders which support trusses at right angles. The girders can be built up from angles to any length or depth that is required for a particular span and the trusses made of the same steel angles rest on the girders. One of the oldest methods using this type of construction is the north light and lattice girder system.

(5) Steel tubing trussing

Welding as a means of structural fabrication has led to the use of steel tubing for roof construction. Generally the quality of the steel is the same as for girders and the tube form has certain advantages: ends can be sealed against corrosion; they are neat in appearance; savings in weight of up to 40 per cent can be made; they collect less dirt. It follows that tubular steelwork can be used in the same roof forms as steel lattice girders, an example of this is in the construction of tubular steel monitor roofs.

(6) Light alloy trussing

Aluminium structures are limited due to initial costs, but they have inherent qualities of lightness, strength, durability and appearance. Because of the effects of heat on aluminium, welding is not usually employed. Girders and beams are riveted or bolted together to form the roof trussing.

Very wide spans have been achieved using aluminium in roof

structures. This can be readily understood when in a roof span of 60 metres the weight of aluminium is approximately one-seventh that of a similar structure in steel.

(7) Reinforced concrete trusses

In Fig. 5.12 is shown a reinforced concrete truss or arched rib used over a large hall in a northern town. There is a bottom tie which prevents the roof from spreading sideways due to the thrust from the

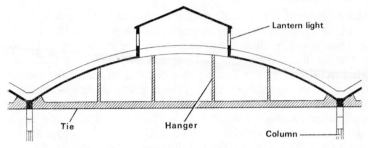

Fig. 5 12 Reinforced concrete trussed or arched rib roof.

arched rib and the tie is itself supported by four hangers. The roof is of reinforced concrete covered with asphalt and a large lantern light runs down the centre of each bay. The whole roof structure is carried on a series of large octagonal reinforced concrete columns with a decorative casing of plywood.

d. The Portal or rigid frame roof

The Portal frame consists essentially of a continuous member conforming to the outline of the roof and connected to vertical columns. The continuous frame has the effect of extending the roof loading to the rest of the structure. Typical Portal or rigid frame construction is shown in Fig. 5.13.

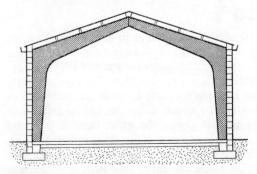

Fig. 5.13 Typical Portal or rigid frame roof construction.

Portal frames are particularly suitable for single-storey buildings, warehouses, factories, etc. The simple roof form gives a clean internal appearance and reduced maintenance costs when compared to trussing. Steel, aluminium and laminated timber may be used in this type of structure, but the widest application is in the use of reinforced or pre-stressed concrete. Spans of up to 25 metres are common.

e. Shell roofs

As a permanent construction for the roofing of large areas, the shell roof (Fig. 5.14) has much to commend it for its economy in the use of steel and concrete. Shell construction is a type of membrane curved in one or more directions and covered with felt or asphalt and bitumen; it can be constructed of a number of materials: timber, aluminium or even steel sheet, but the majority of shell roofs are of reinforced concrete. Some forms of shell roofs are limited in their application because of difficulties in construction and because of this, the two most popular types of shell roof to be found are the barrel vault shell (Fig. 5.14(1) and the north light shell (Fig. 5.14(2)).

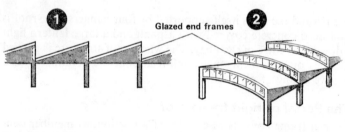

Fig. 5.14 Shell roof construction. (1) Long span multi-bay barrel vaults; (2) north light barrel vault construction.

f. Other types of roof

Many buildings, in particular high buildings in the Greater London Council area, have pitched roofs of fire-resisting construction. Occasionally the two slopes are connected by a flat roof on top. The trusses are of protected steel, the decking (both pitched and flat) is of hollow tile or reinforced concrete, while the pitched portions carry wooden battens to which slates or tiles are fixed. It is not easy to discover at first glance the exact construction and therefore whether roofs of this type are fire-resisting or not. An unusual form of construction, but one which may well come into more common use, is that where the entire roof is monolithic reinforced concrete.

g. Roofing materials

(1) Slates, tiles and shingles

The simplest form of pitched roof covering consists of slates or tiles nailed to or laid on wooden battens, which are themselves nailed to the rafters, although felt is sometimes placed under the battens for purpose of heat insulation and weatherproofing. In better quality work, boarding (as shown in Fig. 5.5) is also sometimes used, and in the best quality work, both boarding and felt are employed, the tiling battens being nailed through them to the rafters below. Slates may be thin and comparatively light in weight or they may be thick and heavy. All slates must be nailed on. Plain tiles are flat or slightly curved on both sides and have 'nibs' at the top which are used to hook them on to the battens. Tiles rest in position by their own weight and only in the best work are they secured (by rails) to the battens. Pantiles are heavier and curly in shape and are hooked on in most cases. Concrete tiles will also be found made to resemble both the interlocking and the plain clay tiles.

To prevent the entry of rain in old roofs or where there is a severe weather exposure, slates and tiles are sometimes bedded in mortar – a process known as 'torching'.

Shingles are similar to slates, but are made of wood. They are not widely used in this country. Tiles are also made of cement asbestos and are extensively used in this form for bungalows, wooden sports pavilions and other inexpensive structures. They can be distinguished by the considerably larger area covered by each individual tile. Owing to their light weight they require less heavy roof members.

(2) Sheeting

Corrugated iron, aluminium and corrugated asbestos-cement sheet require a rather different form of roof construction because the large sheets of material are fixed to purlins and not to battens. With these materials, no common rafters are used. The principal rafters (or trusses in large buildings) are widely spaced – as much as 2 metres or even 3·5 metres apart in the case of principal rafters and 3 to 5 metres in the case of trusses – and themselves support the purlins. There is a line of purlins to each row of corrugated sheet placed under the line where the sheets lap over one another.

Roofs of corrugated iron and corrugated asbestos-cement sheet have poor heat insulation. To meet this an 'underlining' or 'underdrawing' of timber matchboarding, wallboard or plaster board is often placed under the roof covering.

(3) Decking

Decking consists of asbestos cement, timber, woodwool, strawboard, aluminium and steel units. All are used as a decking and need a waterproof layer of asphalt or roofing felt. Decking is more usually applied to flat roofs; the sheets are supported on frameworks of steel, reinforced concrete or timber.

(4) Bituminous felt

Roof surfaces of bituminous felt must be laid on boarding or flat steel sheet. This steel sheet is reinforced with ribs and is also supported on purlins, in the same way as corrugated iron (Fig. 5.15).

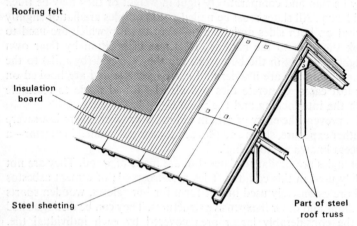

Fig. 5.15 Steel sheet covered roof, with bituminous roofing felt on top.

h. Behaviour of roofs and roofing materials in a fire

The coverings used are in general non-combustible (exceptions, of course, being thatch, wooden shingles and certain types of tarred felt used on small or portable buildings), so that a roof is not normally vulnerable to the transmission of fire by burning brands. Generally speaking, roofs present difficulties to the fireman because of the way they are built rather than the materials of which they are made. Of all types, the pitched roof in general presents the greatest problems in a fire because there is often a large unused space – known variously as the loft, cock loft, attic, roof void, etc. – between the weather covering and the ceiling of the rooms below. It is not uncommon for this space to extend unbroken over the whole area of the building, while the habitable space below is sub-divided into a number of rooms by walls and partitions. Since heat and smoke naturally travel upwards towards the roof, and because the roof itself is generally built of wood, the dangers of this form of construction are apparent. Furthermore, access to the loft is often difficult because trapdoors are not always fitted and a hole must then be cut through a ceiling in order to force a way in.

Plate 17.   Extensive roof collapse of a corrugated iron roof when involved in fire.

Plate 18. A good example of the ability of a closed door to resist the spread of fire. The manner in which hot gases rise is excellently shown by the unaffected lower portions of the woodwork.

Plate 19. The effect of heat on wired glass. Note how the window has remained intact and delayed the venting of the fire.

Plate 20. An example of lift slab construction.

Plate 21. A lift slab construction showing the storey floor slabs being raised by jacks and parked.

Plate 22. A Portal frame type of construction showing the concrete columns rigidly connected to the structural roof members.

Plate 23. An older type of hotel showing utilisation of roof voids.

Plate 24. A modern hotel of framed construction.

te 25. An older type of hospital building. Note the differing levels at the rear
ich could promote access difficulties.

te 26. A modern multi-storey hospital building showing the integrated fire escape
the right.

Plate 27. A range of projecting shops. Note the lantern lights in the roof of each shop and that the party walls are carried through the roofs.

Apart from fires which actually break out in the roof space from such causes as faulty chimneys, sparks, etc., fire can find its way there by way of the openings between the rafters at eaves level if flames or hot gases are escaping from a window. The roof space is frequently used for various purposes for which it was not originally intended and is subdivided by partitions, etc., creating 'dead' pockets. Such pockets also occur in the mansard roof (Fig. 5.7). The triangular spaces thus made are troublesome in a fire, because they are usually inaccessible, and it is often necessary to cut holes in the plaster to verify that the fire is not spreading through the voids.

It will be realised that a simple batten and slate (or tile) roof lets through smoke easily, and that the battens burn through quickly in a fire thus releasing the slates or tiles which slide off – a danger with which all firemen are familiar (see Plates 15 and 16). This helps to vent a fire and thus may assist in preventing it from spreading laterally. Furthermore, battens alone provide considerably less fuel than does close boarding; the latter makes the roof fairly airtight and thus tends to keep in smoke and heat, an effect which is also caused by torching. Felt which is used below the battens is almost invariably flammable and, when impregnated with bitumen or tar, gives off a thick black smoke which may make working conditions very difficult.

In larger wooden roofs such as those of trussed construction, the heavy sections of the timbers are likely to resist fire for a longer period than the lighter wooden rafters and battens. When roof spaces are used to house machinery, however, and the materials become oil impregnated, there is a danger that the tie beams may burn through quickly and cause the collapse of the whole roof. The Belfast roof has a very bad fire reputation and some urban authorities with local Acts will not sanction its use for this reason. The small pieces of timber ignite easily and spread fire rapidly, especially when associated with the usual covering of timber and tarred felt.

Although trusses of cast iron or steel are non-combustible, they always present a hazard in a serious fire for it is impracticable, because of the great weights involved, to encase a large truss in fire-resisting material. In consequence, a trussed form of construction always represents a serious risk of collapse in a fire having sufficient intensity to heat the steelwork above 600°C.

Both wrought-iron and steel trusses have the same characteristics in a fire and their fire resistance varies with the degree of protection given to them by any underlying ceiling. As they are made of light sections they tend to soften and collapse at an early stage in a fire. Where the underside of the roof is lined with a combustible insulating board, or the top is covered with bituminous felt on boarding, the roof covering itself burns and a fire of this kind is difficult to check when it has got beyond the early stages. In many factories having extensive roofs, fire breaks have been constructed to check the spread of fire.

In cinemas, theatres and large halls, a lattice type of truss is often used, generally covered on the underside with a ceiling of plaster which serves in some measure to protect the steelwork above. It should be noted, however, that the bottom tie is the part most exposed to the heat of the fire and, if it softens, the rest of the roof truss and the roof covering will collapse.

With cast iron there is a danger of cracking and rapid collapse if a jet is played on a hot truss. Precautions should be taken to avoid this as the truss may weigh several tonnes and cause great damage to the floors below if it should fall on them. Though it is non-combustible, the fire resistance of the reinforced concrete truss type of roof is not likely to be high because the spalling of the outer layer of concrete on the lower members will rapidly expose the steel reinforcement to the heat of the fire. An advantage is that the heat generated by a fire in the contents of the building would to some extent (depending on their size) be dissipated through the large lantern lights which are generally a feature of this form of construction.

Corrugated asbestos-cement sheet tends to split and fly off very early in a fire, thus helping to vent it. Corrugated iron withstands fire well but tends to keep it inside the building. With modern light steel roof trusses this is important and extensive roof collapses have occurred in the past with corrugated iron roofs (Plate 17). The newer type of steel sheeting shown in Fig. 5.15 shares this disadvantage. Where there are large and numerous ventilators in the roof or extensive areas of plain unwired glazing, which shatters early in a fire, this may dissipate the heat sufficiently to prevent collapse. The relative reliability of corrugated iron and asbestos when walking on roofs is dealt with in the *Manual, Part 6A: Chapter 35, 'Methods of entry'* (Book 11 in the new format), but it is often difficult in the dark to distinguish one from the other as the size of corrugations is frequently almost the same. A point worth noting is that asbestos is noticeably thicker and the two materials may be distinguished by feeling the bottom edge of a sheet.

j. Fire tests of roof construction

To a greater extent than in the case of the BS 476 tests explained earlier, the testing of roof construction attempts to simulate conditions likely to arise in an actual fire situation. The 'external fire exposure roof tests' are set out in *British Standard 476: Part 3: 1958*. In general the test determines the efficiency of a particular type of roof construction being subjected to radiant heat which would be experienced in certain pre-calculated conditions. The test does not relate in any way the conditions under which the construction would behave in fire within the building, but only to exposure from an external fire (flying brands from an adjacent building, etc.). The test grades the various types of roof construction into different categories depending on their performance in the two distinct parts of the test:

(i) fire penetration test;
(ii) surface spread of flame test.

Before either part of the test is carried out, a preliminary ignition test is made to decide whether both of the main parts of the test should be proceeded with. If, in the preliminary ignition test, the specimen is penetrated by fire, the 'fire penetration test' is not made. If, during the preliminary ignition test the specimen flames for more than 5 minutes after the withdrawal of the test flame, or if the maximum distance of spread in any direction across the region of burning exceeds 380 mm, then the 'spread of flame test' is dispensed with. The designation following the penetration and resistance to ignition tests consist of two letters, e.g. AA, AC, BB, etc. these being determined as follows:

First letter

A. Those specimens which have not been penetrated for 1 hour.
B. Those specimens which are penetrated in not less than $\frac{1}{2}$ hour.
C. Those specimens which are penetrated in less than $\frac{1}{2}$ hour.
D. Those specimens which are penetrated in the preliminary ignition test.

Second letter

A. Those specimens on which there is no spread of flame.
B. Those specimens on which there is not more than 533 mm spread of flame.
C. Those specimens on which there is more than 533 mm spread of flame.
D. Those specimens which 'failed' in the preliminary ignition test.

A suffix 'X' is added to the designation where there is dripping from the underside of the specimen, any mechanical failure, or any development of holes. Test results are expressed by the first letter (penetration) followed by the appropriate second letter (spread of flame) and preceded by the letters EXT.F. or EXT.S. according to whether the test had been made on the construction as used as a flat roof or a sloping roof; when necessary the suffix 'X' is added.

For example EXT.F.AA indicates that the specimen was tested on its external surface as a flat roof construction, was not penetrated by fire within 1 hour, that there was no spread of flame; the highest rating. EXT.S.CCX indicates that the specimen was tested on its external surface as a sloping roof construction, that it was penetrated by fire in less than $\frac{1}{2}$ hour, that there was more than 533 mm spread of flame, that it either failed mechanically, dripped from the underside and/or developed holes during the test; an example of a very poor rating.

The second letter designation must not be confused with the spread of flame test classifications in British Standard 476: Part 7. There is no direct relation between the spread of flame test for materials (see Part 1, Chapter 2) and the designation in the roof test.

As with the fire resistance gradings of elements of structure, the designation of roofs also refers to the particular roof construction including the method and material used in fixing. Very often material is marked as 'conforming to AA grade'. A sheet of material cannot be graded individually any more than a material in isolation can be said to have any specific fire resistance. It is only when the sheets are fixed and jointed in the way in which they will be used in a roof construction that a designation can be given.

It will be seen that the tests outlined above are not fire resistance tests in the accepted sense, but are a measure of performance of roof constructions in their ability to resist penetration by fire from outside and their spread of flame characteristics.

k. Building Regulations: Roofs and coverings

As with external walls, the Regulations strike a balance between the resistance of the roof construction to fire penetration from the outside and the distance of the building from the boundary. Thus, whilst a building having a roof designated AA, AB or AC may be erected at any distance from the boundary, other roofs in descending order of designation are required to be 6, 12 and 22 metres from any part of the boundary. Roofs of factories, storage premises, terraced houses and all buildings of more than 1500 cubic metres, however, are required to have a designation of BC or better irrespective of the distance from the boundary.

Certain thermoplastic materials cannot be tested by the methods described above owing to their low softening temperatures. Many of these materials do not ignite easily and do not spread flame to any great extent. When exposed to radiated heat, however, they may fall into the building, possibly spreading fire and leaving the openings thus exposed to flying brands and direct fire radiation. The Regulations do not prohibit the use of these materials, but restrictions as to the maximum area permitted coupled with adequate space separation from adjacent buildings are placed on their use.

3 Non-load-bearing partition walls

The term 'partition' or 'partition wall' is used when referring to walls whose sole function is the division of a space within a building into separate rooms. Sometimes the internal walls are also used to support the floor above, form compartments or separate one building from another. In these cases, although they act as partitions by virtue of the position in which they are built into a structure, they are referred to by their functional names, i.e. compartment wall, separating wall, etc. and are usually load-bearing. In this section, the term partition is used in the 'space division' sense. An internal partition need only be strong enough to support its own weight and be robust enough mechanically for normal conditions of its use. In many circumstances, however, partitions will provide a certain period of fire resistance. For example, the fire resistance of timber-framed non-load-bearing partitions will be determined as much as anything else by their linings/finishes. Plasterboard linings have an established resistance, dependent upon the thickness applied. 19 mm of plasterboard, or two layers of 9·5 mm fixed to break joints has been shown, to provide a fire resistance of 1 hour. 12·5 mm of plasterboard linings fixed to timber framework provides a full half-hour resistance. Plywood and chipboard linings of appropriate thickness make a contribution to fire resistance. The earlier mentioned charring rate for timber can be used for an appropriate assessment of the potential fire resistance of plywood or chipboard linings.

a. Demountable partitions

In certain types of building, such as offices and factories, it is often desirable to provide partitioning in a form which can be dismantled and re-erected easily to allow its use in another position. These demountable partitions are usually made up of fairly large components. Steel units or sheet materials such as plasterboard, strawboard and plastic-faced boards are frequently used; connections and angles formed by metal sections are sometimes of extruded light alloy. The fireman must be observant in his routine visits to buildings with this type of partitioning, as often whole internal layouts can be altered quite quickly without prior notice being given.

b. Fire tests

In unglazed partitions, the criteria and methods used are precisely the same as those required for load-bearing walls (see page 59), except that no load is placed upon the specimen being tested.

4 Stairways

Prior to the introduction of national Building Regulations, there was little, if any, control over the construction of stairs, and badly designed stairways were fraught with danger in normal usage which was even more accentuated in fire and smoke conditions. The Regulations recognised this and now specify precise minimum dimensions for stairways in dwellings, but not for their illumination. (This aspect is covered in Part 3, Chapter 11, 'Services in buildings'.)

In defining the minimum requirement for the safety of persons using a stairway, the Regulations differentiate between those for common use and those for private use. Common use stairways will therefore only occur in *buildings* sub-divided into flats or maisonettes. Private use stairways are those that occur *within* a house or maisonette, or a 'split-level' flat. In addition to the construction rules, which concern the designer and builder rather than the fireman, the Regulations also require that stairways which form part of any building, not only those referred to above, shall be constructed of non-combustible material. This applies whether the stairway is internal or external. There are certain exceptions to this requirement, however, for small and low-hazard buildings. A provision is also made that combustible material may be added to the upper surface of a stairway, so that the use of carpets, etc. is not precluded.

As a stairway is not designated an 'element of structure', it is not required to have any fire resistance, but must, in most cases, be non-combustible; it is in order to use unprotected metal work. The reasoning here is that as the stairway is non-combustible, there is no structural reason why fire should occur in the stairway. At routine inspections of premises, firemen should ensure that no combustible material is stored in a staircase enclosure as this, of course, would nullify all the structural safeguards.

Although it has been said that firemen would not be directly involved in the actual construction requirements of stairs, they will require to be conversant with the more common building terms used, and with the various types of stairway in use. These are combined in the illustrations shown in Figs. 5.16 to 5.20. A method of safe-guarding stairways from fire and smoke is described in Chapter 7.

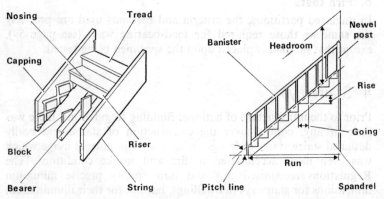

Fig. 5.16 The technical terms as applied to staircases.

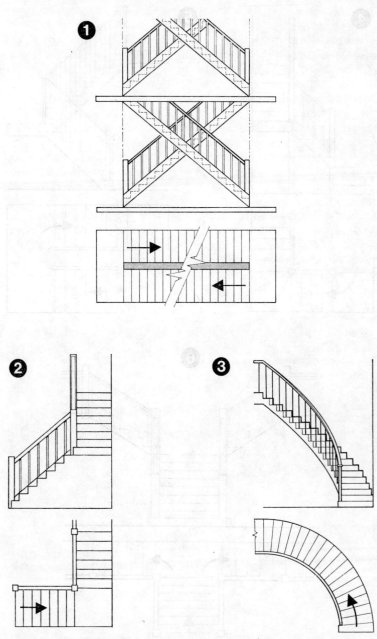

Fig. 5.17 Types of stairway: (1) scissors; (2) quarter turn; (3) geometrical.

89

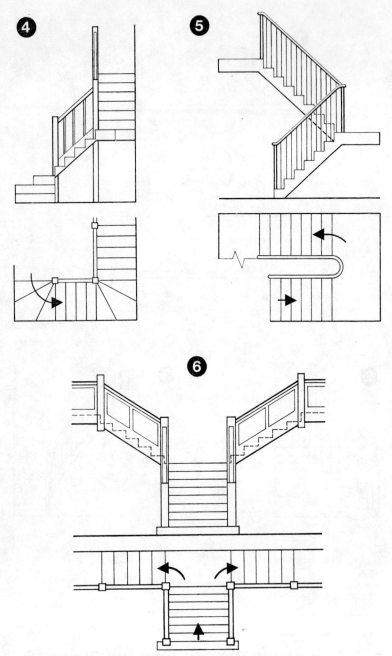

Fig. 5.18 Types of stairway: (4 and 5) half turn; (6) bifurcated.

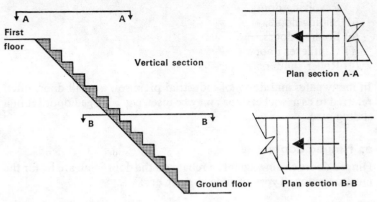

Fig. 5.19 Straight flight stairs.

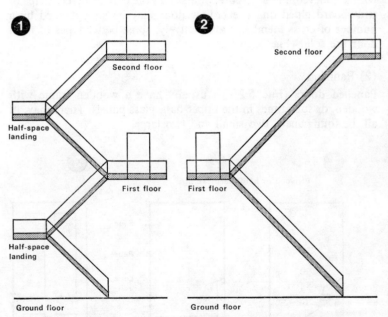

Fig. 5.20 (1) Dog-legged stairs; (2) geometrical flight (open well) stairs.

5 Doors

Doors, shutters and gates are of seven principal types:

    (a) Hinged doors.
    (b) Swing doors.

    (c) Revolving doors.
    (d) Sliding doors.
    (e) Folding doors.
    (f) Cantilever doors.
    (g) Roller shutters.

In many gates and doors of industrial premises, a small door, often referred to as a 'wicket door', may be inset, e.g. a hinged door set in a sliding gate.

a. Hinged doors

Hinged doors closing against a rebate on the door jamb are by far the most common. Types of hinged door are:

(1) Flush

Probably the commonest type of hinged door, and one which is relatively cheap to construct, is the lightweight flush door (Fig. 5.21(1)). This usually consists of two layers of plywood or hardboard with a honeycomb paper core. Sometimes the core is merely strips of strawboard glued on. The hollow door may be strengthened by a number of cross members; alternatively, some better types of flush door are solid (Fig. 5.21(2)).

(2) Panelled

Panelled doors (Fig. 5.21(3)) usually have a wooden frame with wooden, or sometimes in the upper half, glass panels. There may, in all, be four panels, two small and two large.

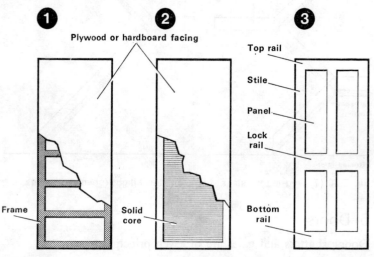

Fig. 5.21 Typical wooden doors: (1) Flush door, skeleton type. (2) Flush door, solid type. (3) Panelled door.

(3) Ledged

Many ledged doors (Fig. 5.22) are of light construction. They may be ledged only (Fig. 5.22(1)), or there may be bracing in addition (Fig. 5.22(2)), or framing (Fig. 5.22(3)) – a common type is framed, ledged and braced.

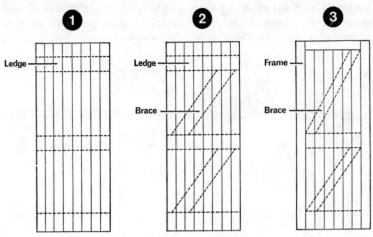

Fig. 5.22 Other types of wooden door: (1) Ledged. (2) Ledged and braced. (3) Framed and braced.

(4) Metal

Examples of steel-covered doors are shown in Fig. 5.23(1 and 2). Doors of this kind may sometimes be steel with wooden linings,

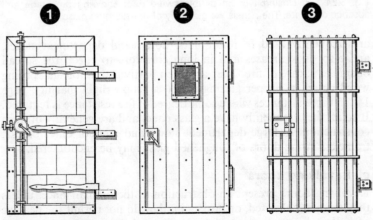

Fig. 5.23 Typical metal doors: (1) and (2). Two types of steel-covered fire-resisting door. (3) Barred door.

93

so that the steel is concealed. Barred doors vary greatly in construction, but a typical example is shown in Fig. 5.23(3).

b. Swing doors

Any of the above types of door may be found with special pin hinges (Fig. 5.24) allowing them to swing in either direction, and consequently there is no rebate on the jamb. Such doors may consist of a single or a double leaf in a single opening. Swing doors

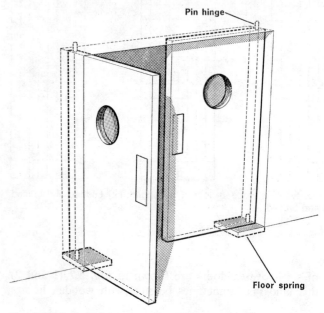

Fig. 5.24 Self-closing type of double swing door showing pin hinge and absence of rebate. The panels are generally of fire-resisting glass.

are frequently used in restaurants, hotels and department stores, and also on staircases and in long corridors to check the spread of smoke in case of fire. They are often partly glazed, the glass being wired or set in copper glazing bars (see 'copperlight glazing', page 14), in those instances where some degree of fire resistance is required. If solid, they frequently have a glass panel and are generally of flush construction. In large department stores and modern office blocks, frameless swing doors of toughened glass may be encountered.

c. Revolving doors

Revolving doors present an obstruction to the fireman since, unless they are first collapsed, or broken in, they do not permit the passage of bulky objects or lines of hose. These doors revolve on central pivots at the top and bottom and usually have four wings arranged at right angles to one another. In some types of door only two wings may be found, each of which has a curved extension piece. The wings on the doors are generally constructed to collapse and to move to one side so as to give a relatively unobstructed opening. There are two common methods of securing the wings, and these are shown in Fig. 5.25.

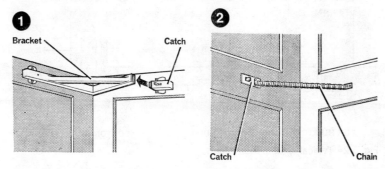

Fig. 5.25 Two common methods of securing the wings of revolving doors. (1) The stretcher bar type. (2) Chain type.

In the first of these (Fig. 5.25(1)) the wings are held in place by a bracket or solid stretcher bar situated usually at the top of the door across the angle formed by the leaves where they join the newel post. One end of each bar is permanently connected to one leaf of the door and the other engages with some form of catch on the adjacent leaf. The wings are collapsed by releasing the stretcher bars, either by undoing the wing nuts or by unfastening the catches which hold them in place.

In the second type (Fig. 5.25(2)), the two opposing wings are hinged to the single leaf formed by the other two and are kept in position by a chain which runs through them and is held by a catch on each of the hinged leaves. If this catch is released, the wings can be folded back to give a clear opening.

d. Sliding doors

These doors may be either of solid construction or in the form of a lattice which collapses into a relatively small space when opened. Sliding doors may run in tracks above and below the door (Fig. 5.26) or be suspended from an overhead track (Fig. 5.27). They are not often encountered in domestic property except possibly in garages, but those of solid construction are widely used in commercial premises, especially as fire-resisting doors for isolating sections of a building (see par. (h)). These doors may either slide on one or both sides of the opening, or alternatively may move into a central recess in the wall.

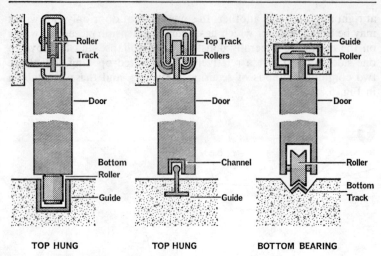

Fig. 5.26 Typical sliding door tracks.

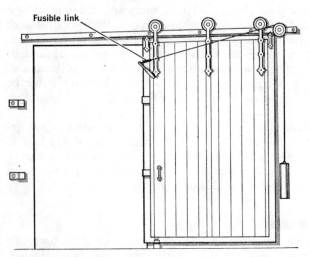

Fig. 5.27 One type of sliding door running on an overhead track and operated by a fusible link.

Steel lattice doors (Fig. 5.28) are widely used to protect property where weatherproofing is unimportant. The gate usually runs on two sets of tracks, one above and the other beneath, but may sometimes be found with a bottom track only. They are often to be found as a protection to the opening of a lift or lift shaft.

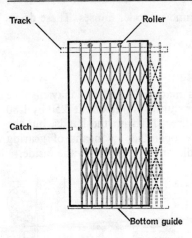

Fig. 5.28 Typical steel lattice gate.

e. Folding doors

Folding doors are usually of fairly light construction, but exceptionally, they may be very large and of robust construction. They are often found as separating doors between two rooms where space is valuable. They are similar in design to normal hinged doors, but the two or more leaves are hinged together so that the whole door opens to one side only.

f. Cantilever doors

This door (Fig. 5.29) is counterbalanced and pivoted so that the whole door rises upwards and, when open, lies horizontally. Cantilever doors are usually to be found on garages, but steel-plated doors

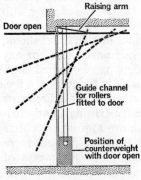
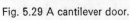
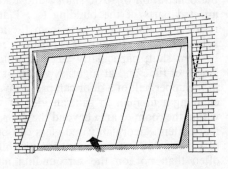

Fig. 5.29 A cantilever door.

of this type are also sometimes found in boiler houses. These doors generally fit flush in the opening.

g. Roller shutters

Roller shutters are nearly always made of steel, but may also be found made of timber. Small roller shutters up to about 2.50 by 1.80 metres are generally raised by a direct lift with the hands, but the larger sizes are almost invariably operated by means of gearing (Fig. 5.30) and some form of handle or chain block on the inside.

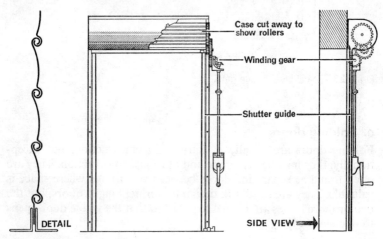

Fig. 5.30 Typical gear-operated roller shutter, showing on the left in detail the section of the shutter.

h. Fire resistance of doors

Apart from its normal function, a door serves to contain an outbreak of fire within the room or compartment of origin and should prevent the penetration of toxic smoke and toxic fumes into otherwise un-affected parts of the building (see Plate 18). A closed door also restricts the flow of oxygen from the atmosphere outside, thereby helping to starve the fire. It is for these reasons that all doors should be kept shut, particularly when a building is unoccupied for any length of time and at night. A vision or safety panel of wired glass, in the upper half of a door can prove invaluable in the event of a fire, enabling a fireman to gain an idea of whether or not a fire exists within the room or area beyond the door, and, if existing, its approximate extent. Georgian wired glass can be shown to resist the effects of fire for an hour or more, but its ability to do so depends more often than not on the surrounding materials and the means of retention employed. The area of glazing should be strictly controlled but will vary with the situation of the use of a particular door.

The Building Regulations quote two types of door which have become known as 'firecheck-' and fire-resisting'. The former is used in situations when the primary function of the door is to prevent or restrict the spread of hot gases and smoke. It must be capable of holding back fire for 20 minutes (integrity) and must not collapse within 30 minutes (stability). The use of such doors is limited to entrance doors separating flats and maisonettes from common access areas, and to connecting doors between houses and attached small garages and doors to habitable rooms and kitchens in stairways in residential buildings of three or more storeys. Examples of fire-check doors made to *British Standard 459: Part 3: 1951* are shown in Fig. 5.31. Fire resistance requirements for doors do not normally

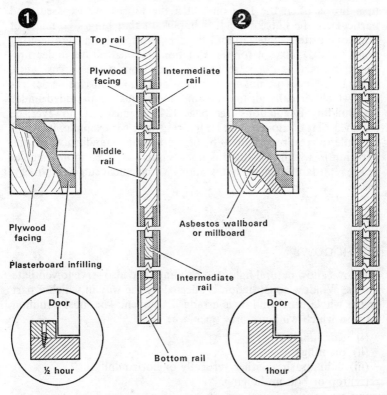

Fig. 5.31 Examples of fire-check doors made to BS 459, Part 3, 1951. (1) A fire-check door of 30/20 minutes standard. (2) A door of 60/40 minutes standard

impose a minimum period of insulation. The test report under BS 476 will include this, however, and from the result, it is possible to frame a recommendation of safe distance for the locating of combustible material from the face of the door.

99

On the other hand, a fire-resisting door is used in situations where its function is to retard fire spread for a specified period. Timber doors can be used satisfactorily for periods of fire resistance up to 60 minutes, but for periods above this, steel or composite construction becomes necessary. Some authorities permit existing panelled doors to be modified by the infilling of the panels with plasterboard or asbestos insulation board (NOT asbestos cement sheeting) provided the door is otherwise of substantial construction.

The fit of a door in its frame is a significant factor and it will be seen from Fig. 5.31 that in the door frame of a 60-minutes fire-check door, the door stop is required to be cut from the solid timber frame, whereas in the 30-minutes fire-check door, it is permissible for the stop to be screwed on to the frame. The weak point of a door in a fire is often the face on which the hinges are exposed, and particularly the hinge side; it is important that hinges be made of non-combustible material, and they require to have a high melting point (800°C). Except for the situation outlined above under fire-check doors (i.e. doors separating flats from access areas, etc.), rising butt hinges are not acceptable as automatic self-closing devices with which virtually all fire-resisting doors must be provided under the Building Regulations (see page 124). It must not, however, be assumed that all doors must be fire-resisting; for example, it would be futile to require a door to be of fire-resisting standard where the partition in which it is fitted is not required to perform any smoke or fire retardant function, but is simply a convenient sub-division of a space.

6 Windows

Windows allow natural light into buildings and also serve to ventilate rooms. Window construction is affected by the way in which a part or the whole of a window is arranged to open. The most common ways in which windows may open are:

   (i)   side hinging;
   (ii) pivoting;
   (iii) sliding sashes, either vertically or horizontally;
   (iv) top or bottom hinging.

Windows are generally referred to as of two types according to the method of opening, these being 'casement' or 'sash'.

a. Casement windows

The simplest (Fig. 5.32) consists of a square or rectangular window frame of timber or metal with the window casement-hung, i.e. hinged at one side. When more than one casement is openable it is usual to refer to them as being two, three or four-light casements. Often a two or more light casement window is in the form of vent-lights. These are top-hung to open outwards (Fig. 5.32(2)). The horizontal framing between the casement and the ventlight is called the transom. Some windows of this type are constructed so that only a part is openable. That part of the window which does not open is called a deadlight.

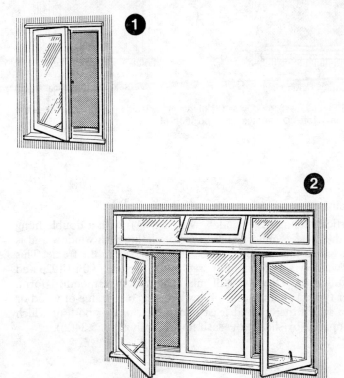

Fig. 5.32 Casement windows: (1) single-light casement window; (2) two-light casement with vent lights.

b. Sash windows

(1) Pivoted sash windows

The opening part of this type of window is supported by pivots at each side (Fig. 5.33(1)), or at the top and bottom of the frame (Fig. 5.33(2)) so that they open partly into and partly out of the room. The word sash is used to describe the opening portion of a window and includes the glass and its timber or metal frame.

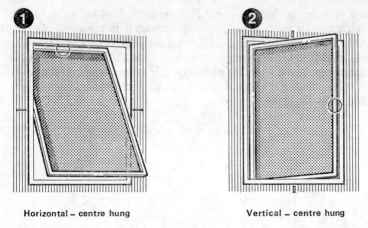

Horizontal – centre hung   Vertical – centre hung

Fig. 5.33 Pivoted sash windows: (1) pivots at each side. (2) Pivoted at the top and bottom. Note: O denotes usual position of catch.

(2) Sliding sash windows

The vertical sliding sash window (Fig. 5.34(1)) with a double hung sash is the most commonly used type of sliding sash window and is constructed so that the two sashes slide vertically in the frame. This type of window was commonly used in the period 1700 to 1920 and many still exist. They are still manufactured in a modified form. Another type of sliding sash window consists of a frame of wood or metal in which there are at least two sashes, one or both of which can be opened by sliding the sash horizontally (Fig. 5.34(2)).

Fig. 5.34 Sliding sash windows. (1) Double-hung vertically sliding sash window. (2) Horizontal sliding sash window.

c. Double glazed windows

One sheet of glass in a window is a very poor insulator against the transfer of heat. In order to reduce heat loss two sheets of glass at lease 5 mm apart are fixed in the casement or sash with clean dry air trapped between them and often hermetically sealed (Fig. 5.35). This does not increase the fire resistance of the glazing to any significant extent and in fact this type of glazing can shatter with explosive force when involved in fire.

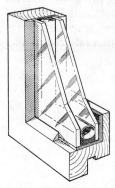

Fig. 5.35 Cut-away view of a double glazing unit.

d. Leaded windows

Leaded windows consist of a number of small panes of glass held together by strip lead. Such windows, especially those of coloured glass to be found in churches and cathedrals, may be of considerable value. The value lies in the glass, not in the leading which can be replaced. The leaded panes are often held in position by light gauge bars running from side to side of the opening.

e. French windows

French windows are not strictly speaking windows, but should be regarded either as a pair of panel doors or as casement windows as appropriate.

7 Roof lights

A roof light is a form of window in the plane of the roof and fixed. An opening roof light is referred to as a 'skylight'.

Almost all modern factories and other large single storey buildings are provided with some form of roof lighting. This can take one or more of the following forms:

 (a) lantern light;
 (b) monitor light;
 (c) dome light;
 (d) lens light;
 (e) dead light.

a. Lantern lights

Lantern lights (Fig. 5.36) consist of vertical glazed sides and a glazed roof. The sides are often arranged to open or are fitted with louvres for ventilation. They will allow the escape of smoke and hot gases from a fire within the building. A lantern light without the vertical upstands is strictly speaking a skylight, but is often referred to as a 'decklight'.

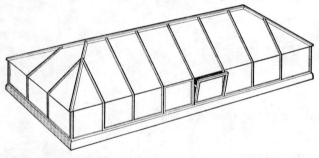

Fig. 5.36 Example of a lantern light with openable sides.

b. Monitor roof lights

These (Fig. 5.37) take the form of glass 'boxes' each with a flat top on flat or low-pitched roofs. The sides are usually arranged to open as in (a) above.

Fig. 5.37 Monitor roof lights.

c. Dome lights

A fairly wide range of standard-sized glass, thermoplastics or fibre glass dome lights both circular and rectangular, is used in flat roof construction. A typical dome light is illustrated in Fig. 5.38.

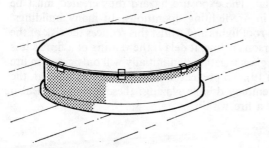

Fig. 5.38 A typical dome light.

d. Lens light

Lens lights (Fig. 5.39) consist of square or circular glass blocks of substantial strength cast into the reinforced concrete ribs of flat and barrel type roofs. They do not provide any ventilation and do not allow the escape of smoke or heat, though they are sometimes associated with upstands from the flat roof into which top-hung opening windows or louvres are incorporated.

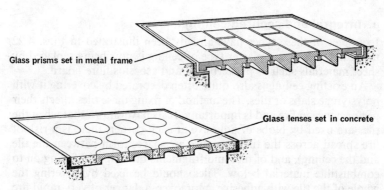

Glass prisms set in metal frame

Glass lenses set in concrete

Fig. 5.39 Two principal types of lens light. These types of light are also found in pavements.

e. Dead lights

This term signifies areas of glazing or translucent sheeting fixed in the slope of a roof, or lens lights in a flat or barrel roof, so that they do not open.

f. General

It will be noted that most types of roof light will fail in heat, venting a fire to the outside air. This stops the fire from spreading laterally within the building. Hazardous conditions can arise from this, however, if the escaping heat and flames can reach adjacent buildings or flammable material. The exposure hazard thus created must be adequately covered in fire-fighting operations. In many buildings, wired glass is used in roof lights and whilst this reduces the risk of the glass falling on to persons below, it delays the venting of a fire as it is designed to hold the glass together and initially will only crack in fire conditions (see Plate 19). To prevent natural heat losses through the roof, some systems employ double glazing; these systems will also delay the venting of a fire within.

8 Ceilings

Ceilings have a valuable contribution to make in the protection of a building against fire. Whilst the true element of structure is the floor above the ceiling, the fire resistance of which is measured by the number of minutes it can withstand fire, a ceiling, whilst possibly providing a certain additional amount of fire resistance, must have properties which resist the spread of flame across its surface. Two basic types of ceiling are used:

(a) those which are integral with, or are secured to, the underside (soffit) of the floor;

(b) those which are suspended from the underside of the floor.

a. Integral and secured ceilings

Examples of these types have already been illustrated in Figs. 4.22 to 4.24. The lath and plaster type of ceiling is now being replaced by sheet materials such as plasterboard and asbestos fibre board.

An existing ceiling is also quite often decorated by covering it with polystyrene slabs or tiles. The method of fixing these tiles affects their performance in fire and is important. Tests have shown that when the tiles are fixed by blobs of adhesive at each corner, there is a risk of fire spread across the tiles (because air spaces form between the tile and the ceiling), and of tiles and fragments burning and falling on to combustible material below. Tiles should be fixed by covering the whole of the tile with adhesive. Moreover, a danger of very rapid fire spread can be created if polystyrene tiles are painted with oil-based paint; only water-based emulsion or flame retardant paints should be used.

Firemen should be alert to the fact that in some properties 'modernisation' has included the addition of a suspended ceiling under the original lath and plaster, the latter's fire protective qualities being drastically reduced by cutting away to accommodate the support struts or wires for the new tile ceiling.

b. Suspended ceilings

Suspended ceilings, which were often termed 'false ceilings', may be sub-divided into three groups, as follows:

(i)   in which the ceiling is flat;
(ii) in which architectural forms, plaster decorated domes, coverings, etc. are framed into the ceiling;
(iii) in which the ceiling protects the steelwork of the floor above.

Types (i) and (ii) refer to the older forms of construction. In modern constructional methods, the problems presented by suspended ceilings in fire, i.e. the unobserved entry and spread of fire in the space between floor and ceiling, have been recognised. Good practice requires that no combustible material, except perhaps the covering of electric wiring, be built into the space, and that the hangers from which the ceiling is supported be also non-combustible.

At each point of separation of the building, compartment walls, separating walls and those partitions which are required to be fire resisting, are extended to the underside of the floor, if not by similar partitioning, then by fire resisting material between the ceiling and floor. This is called fire stopping. Any openings in the floor itself for services, pipes, etc. will also be effectively fire stopped. Fig. 5.40 shows an example of a modern suspended ceiling as might be found in cinemas or large halls.

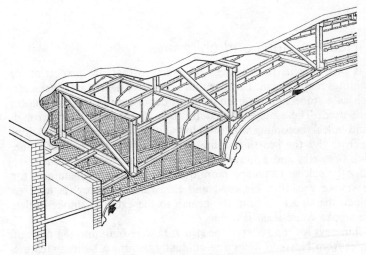

Fig. 5.40 An example of a modern suspended ceiling as found in cinemas or large halls.

Suspended ceilings protecting steel beams (type (iii)) are constructed specifically to contribute to the fire resistance of the floor above. In this case (Fig. 5.41) the whole assembly, i.e. both floor and suspended ceiling, becomes the element of structure and is assessed for its period of fire resistance accordingly. BS 476, Part 8, 1972, sets out the details of such tests. This is often referred to as a membrane protection. Unfortunately, the fireman will find it hard to tell whether a given ceiling is of the fire resisting type or not. In the event of a ceiling collapsing, care should be taken to note, if possible, whether unprotected steel work is revealed above, in which case fire-fighting operations may have to be modified accordingly.

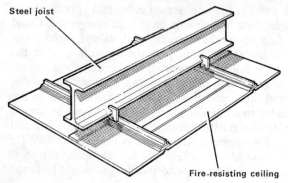

Fig. 5.41 A modern suspended ceiling protecting a steel joist.

9 Hearths, flues and chimneys

It is probably in this element of structure that fire protection of buildings really began. In older times primitive hearth arrangements, such as a stone slab or a scooped out depression in the earth floor, were used. The smoke filtered through thatch and later through 'wind holes' (becoming windows) in the walls at high level. Developing from this the hearth and fire were built on a low wall of stone, brick or earth, and a louvred opening was provided in the roof to allow the smoke to escape more quickly; this route (cheminee) for the smoke was then enclosed and the word 'chimney' is used to include the structure from the hearth to the external smoke outlet. The smoke route itself is a flue.

Chimneys forming part of the structure were built into the walls of castles from Norman times and gradually became a building feature in many houses. An early reference to brick (then spelt 'breke') was made in 1427 in respect of a purchase of bricks to make a chimney.

Improvements in materials and design were adopted over the years until as late as 1844 local authorities were given power to control building and set standards. These included quite stringent requirements for hearths. At the present time the Building Regulations specify the methods of construction of hearths, chimneys and flues, and Fig. 5.42 shows a method of constructing a hearth to comply with the Regulations. The Regulations are quite complex and it would be inappropriate to attempt to explain them in detail. In essence, the Regulations require any chimney, flue-pipe, constructional hearth or fireplace recess to be constructed of non-combustible materials of such a nature, quality and thickness as not to be unduly affected by heat, condensate and products of combustion; also to be so constructed and of such a thickness, or in the case of a flue-pipe, so placed or shielded, as to prevent the ignition of any part of the building.

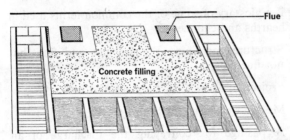

Fig. 5.42 Method of constructing a hearth by cutting back the joists and inserting a concrete filling, usually laid on a trimmer arch (see Fig. 5.43).

Most hearth fires occur due to faulty construction (Fig. 5.43(1)) and it must be borne in mind that many hearths were constructed prior to byelaws and regulations. Many also are the work of the

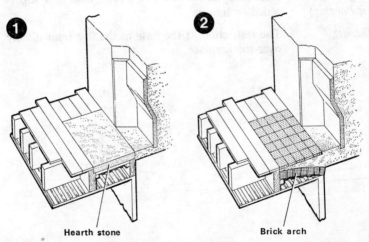

Fig. 5.43 (1) Incorrect type of hearth construction liable to lead to fires. The thin slab of concrete below the hearth is laid direct on to tongued and grooved boarding. (2) A well-constructed hearth as shown in Fig. 5.42 showing trimmer arch and concrete carrying the tiled hearth.

'Do-it-yourself' (DIY) enthusiast, who will often not appreciate the precautions to be taken in this type of construction, and whose work is not inspected by the Building Authority. Some common causes of hearth fires are:

(i) cracked hearths allowing sparks and hot embers to ignite materials below or adjacent to the hearth;

(ii) joists not properly trimmed to a safe distance with insufficient thickness of hearthstone separating them from the fire;

(iii) timber shuttering in which the original concrete of the hearth has been poured being left in place.

The following is a glossary of some of the common terms used in connection with hearths and chimneys.

Chimney: Structure containing the fireplace and flue (but not flue-pipe).

Chimney breast: Projection of wall for fireplace and flue.

Flaunching: Mortar weathering at top of stack.

Flue: A passage for conveying the discharge of an appliance to the external air.

Flue-pipe: Pipe forming a flue but not a pipe built as a lining into a chimney.

Flue lining: Clay or other lining to a flue integral with the chimney structure.

Pargetting: Rendering on the inside of a brick flue, now super-
(or *Parging*)   seded by linings.

Throat: The restriction at the base of the flue immediately over the fireplace.

Part 3
Building design

This Part takes the review of structural fire safety to its third and final stage. First, in Part 1, came the fundamental study of the fire properties of the materials themselves. Next, in Part 2, came consideration of the components into which these materials are formed and from which building as a whole is constituted. Finally, in this Part, an examination is provided of the design and layout of complete buildings and the prospects they offer of safety from danger to themselves and their contents in the event of fire, and to each other. This examination is extended to include those features of building design which tend towards safety in fire by facilitating fire fighting.

It is only in comparatively modern times that any real attempt has been made to secure safety from fire by controlling the design of buildings, although the idea of the 'party wall', whose purpose was to prevent a fire in one house from overrunning a whole street, is centuries old. It is probable that the first step towards designing a safe interior was taken in the early or middle part of the 19th century when a series of devastating fires in theatres focused attention on the proscenium, which was later termed the proscenium wall. Originally, in Greek and Roman times, the proscenium had been at the back of the stage and had had purely scenic functions; these changed from century to century. Indeed, a proscenium often went completely out of fashion. By the beginning of the 19th century, however, it featured at the front of the stage in all theatre designs and the efforts made towards saving lives were focused upon it, reaching the point at the end of the century where it can be studied in examples still standing. Its effect is to divide the material of the building into two parts; the stage on one side and the auditorium on the other. These two parts, at the time when the design developed, were of severe but contrasting types of risk; the stage area of very high fire hazard, at a time when lighting and many stage effects were produced by candle, torch and gas flames, and both scenery and costumes were copious and highly flammable; and the auditorium containing a closely packed, seated audience with sometimes hundreds standing. The wall divided these two, and the safety curtain closed the proscenium opening in the event of fire; in later designs an automatically opening vent over the stage served to direct a fire upwards to open air and thus away from the audience.

This theatre design was the classic statement of the fundamental principle of planning buildings for fire safety: where an area of high fire risk exists in any building, that area should be separated from other areas, especially those of high life risk. This is a comparatively simple application of a concept which can become complex when a building comprises many storeys, or many varieties of risk, or both, and when escape problems (with which we are not concerned in this Book) are woven into the fabric of the building.

An important extension of this principle emerged much later; the introduction of the time factor. In the theatre the only time factor operating was the time it would take the audience to leave; if the wall and safety curtain would last this long their function would have been adequately discharged. If, however, the fire spread into the auditorium after the audience had left this would result in the total destruction of the building unless the fire brigade could prevent it. It began to be accepted that a fire of real magnitude was a threat to public safety in the locality and should be prevented by law; it is pre-supposed that any large building can be divided up in such a way that a fire in one part of it will not destroy the whole. It is easy to see that implementation of this principle led, in the Model Building Bye-laws, to a requirement for a large building to be sub-divided by stout walls, each forming a boundary of a portion of the building possessing a given maximum volume, with stout doors to close any necessary openings in the walls. But how stout? Obviously, stout enough to withstand the effects of a fire on either side of the wall for as long as the fire was likely to last.

Hence the need for fire resistance testing, which was dealt with in the previous Part. Building regulations in many countries require the special division of buildings into compartments by fire-resisting construction whose standard, in terms of hours of duration, varies according to the building's occupancy, the size of the compartment, its height above ground and other factors. This Part explains these arrangements in detail and goes further to describe restrictions that are imposed on building design in order to retard the spread of fire from one building to another.

Chapter 6
Separating walls

It was stated in Chapter 4, Section 3, that in current building practice walls have specific functions and are named accordingly. A *separating wall* means a wall or part of a wall which is common to two adjoining buildings. As an example, each house in a terrace is considered to be a separate building and the walls between these houses are, therefore, separating and not compartment walls. In legal parlance this is termed a 'party' wall, but because this refers to ownership and responsibilities other than fire resistance, the term 'separating wall' is used nowadays in the context of building construction, though not in the London Building Acts.

1 Requirements

Separating walls, except for certain permitted openings described below, must:

(i) be imperforate;

(ii) have a fire resistance from both sides of at least 60 minutes;

(iii) be adequately sealed at the junction of external walls and roofs (i.e. fire stopped);

(iv) be non-combustible, apart from the surface finish, except for certain small uncompartmented buildings.

2 Permitted openings

Pipes (other than flue pipes) can pass through a separating wall provided they are not of greater diameter than 38 mm if combustible, or 150 mm if non-combustible. The opening through which the pipes pass must be fire stopped (Fig. 6.1(1)). A door may be placed in a separating wall if it is necessary as a means of escape from fire (Fig. 6.1(2)), the door however, must have not less than the standard of fire resistance required for the separating wall.

113

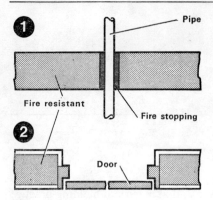

Fig. 6.1 Separating walls must be totally imperforate except for the permitted openings shown, and must have a fire resistance of not less than one hour. (1) Fire stopping of openings for pipes. (2) Doors must have same fire resistance as separating wall.

3 Roof and wall junctions

The Regulations are designed to ensure that fire will not pass through cracks or loose joints at the junction of separating walls with roofs and other elements of structure. The principle on which this is based is shown in Fig. 6.2. The first method by which this is attained is by requiring the separating wall to penetrate the roof to a height of not less than 375 mm (Fig. 6.2(1)), and no combustible material must be built into or through the wall in such a way as to impair its effectiveness.

Clearly this method is unjustified in the case of non-combustible slab-type roofs. In these cases, the separating wall is fire stopped (Fig. 6.2(2)) on the underside of the slab, and the surface covering of the roof must be designated AA, AB or AC (see page 85). The general rule is also waived in respect of buildings in the public residential, office or public assembly groups not more than 12·5 metres in height and in which any part of the roof within 1·5 metres of the separating wall is covered with non-combustible material or asphalt and the junction between the wall and roof is fire stopped (Fig. 6.2(3) and (4)).

Similarly at junctions of separating and external walls (Fig. 6.3), fire stopping is required if any surface within the cavity is combustible and is lower than Class 0.

It would be wrong to suggest that buildings to the standard of separation outlined above have only been constructed since the implementation of the national regulations in 1966; the Bye-laws prior to that date had similar standards of separation. However, it

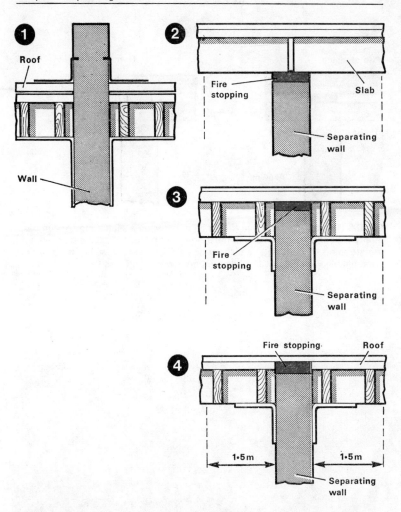

Fig. 6.2 Methods by which fire is prevented from penetrating separating walls. (1) Separating (or compartment) wall penetrating roof. (2 to 4) Alternative methods of treating junction of separating wall with roof; (2) applicable to all buildings; (3) when both buildings are residential, office or assembly buildings; (4) when both buildings are small residential buildings of not more than three storeys.

must be remembered that older buildings are more likely to have had breaches made in their separating walls, and fire spread in such cases is likely to occur more readily; this in turn may affect the stability and integrity of the separating wall.

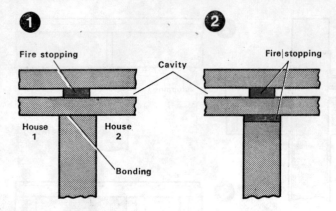

Fig. 6.3 Diagram showing that the junction between a separating (or compartment) wall and an external wall must be (1) bonded, or (2) fire-stopped, and fire stopping of the cavity is also required if any surface within the cavity is combustible with a spread of flame rating lower than Class O.

Chapter 7
Compartmentation

To prevent a fire in a building from spreading from its area of origin to other parts of the building, the walls and floors enclosing each part of that building must form effective barriers to fire. Not only must these elements of structure be of adequate fire resistance, but the compartments themselves must have certain limitations imposed upon them, where appropriate, in respect of size. A simple example of this principle is found in an engineering workshop where the risk from the main production is extremely low, but that from the finishing process, by paint spraying for instance, is relatively high. In such a case, the finishing process is separated from the production side by enclosing the spray shop with fire-resisting construction (Fig. 7.1). This method of segregation can be applied from this

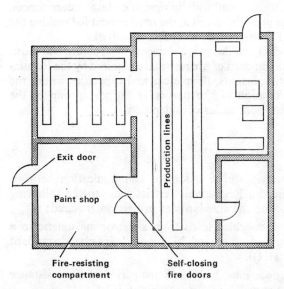

Fig. 7.1 Diagram showing the compartmentation of an engineering workshop. Also shown are the production lines with their high fire risks.

fundamental example to the most complex of multi-occupancy development projects. This breaking up of a building into fire-tight cells is termed *compartmentation*. As has already been said, it is not a novel concept by any means, but only comparatively recently has it been made mandatory for many groups of building.

1 Limitation of size

The Building Regulations prescribe limits of size for certain buildings or compartments according to their purpose group. No limits are placed on the single-storey buildings, except for those in the 'institutional' and 'other residential' groups (single-storey hospitals, hotels, etc.), in which the floor area is limited to 3000 square metres. In buildings of more than one storey, limits are imposed on height, floor area and/or cubic capacity of all purpose groups except those comprising the small residential, office and assembly groups. In the shops group, the Regulations provide that where an automatic sprinkler system is fitted throughout, the maximum floor area and cubic capacity prescribed can be doubled.

2 Compartment walls and floors

The boundaries of compartments of buildings to which limits of size apply will be formed by 'compartment walls' and 'compartment floors'. These must be constructed of non-combustible material as must any structural members supporting them. There are exceptions in respect of floor finishes and wall linings; in certain circumstances, when old buildings are being altered, the requirement for making the existing walls and floors non-combustible is waived.

Compartment walls and floors are elements of structure and must, therefore, be of the standard of fire resistance required by the Regulations for the varying heights, floor areas and capacities within the maximum size limitation of the particular purpose group of the building or compartment under consideration.

3 Permitted openings

Allowance must obviously be made for communication between compartments, and the Regulations restrict these to the following openings, and also set the standards of protection required:

(i) An access door which leads from a flat or maisonette to a common area must be of 30 minutes' fire-check standard (see Fig. 5.31(1)).

(ii) Any other door must have the same period of fire resistance as that of the wall or floor (see Fig. 6.1(2)).

(iii) An opening for a protected shaft (Fig. 7.2(1)).

(iv) An opening for a ventilation duct (Fig. 7.2(2)).

(v) An opening for a refuse chute (Fig. 7.2(3)).

(vi) An opening for a pipe (not a flue pipe) (Fig. 7.2(4)).

(vii) An opening for a chimney, appliance ventilation duct or duct encasing one or more flue pipes (Fig. 7.2(5 and 6)).

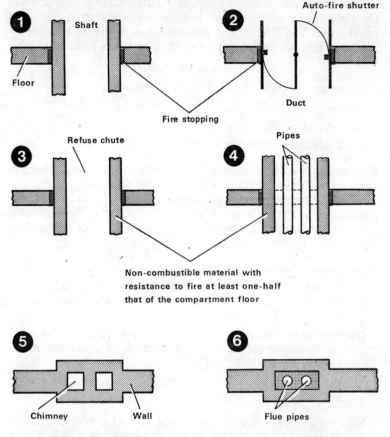

Fig. 7.2 Openings through floors. (1) Opening for a protected shaft. (2) Opening for a ventilated duct. (3) Opening for a refuse chute. (4) Opening for pipes (not flue pipes). (5) Opening for a chimney. (6) Duct encasing flue pipes.

It should be noted in (ii) above that the term 'door' in the context of the Building Regulations also includes shutters, traps, covers or any other form of protection to an opening in any wall or floor of a building.

4 Junctions formed by elements of structure

Junctions which are formed by elements of structure can constitute a particular weakness in a building allowing fire and hot gases to spread to the outside of a compartment involved in fire; this could possibly endanger the whole building unless special precautions are taken to ensure that the joints are tight enough to prevent the passage of fire. This is particularly important in industrialised systems where the walls, floors, etc. are made in a factory and erected piecemeal on the site. The Regulations deal with this aspect of building by requiring that where compartment walls or floors form a junction with:

(i) other compartment floors;

(ii) separating walls;

(iii) external walls; or

(iv) a structure protecting a shaft;

the junction (see Fig. 6.3) must be properly bonded or fire stopped in order to maintain the continuity of fire resistance.

Where a compartment wall forms a junction with a roof, the general rule is the same as for a separating wall, i.e. the wall must extend not less than 375 mm above the surface of the roof (see Fig. 6.2(1)). This rule is waived if:

(v) any part of the roof which is within 1·5 metres of the wall is designated AA, AB or AC in respect of BS 476 tests (see page 85), or it complies with a 'deemed to satisfy' specification (see Fig. 6.2(2)); and

(vi) the deck of that part of the roof (i.e. that within 1·5 metres of the compartment wall) is constructed of non-combustible solid or hollow slab; and

(vii) the junction between the compartment wall and the roof is fire stopped.

No combustible material is permitted to be built into, through, across the top or over the top of any compartment wall in a way which would render ineffective the fire resistance of the wall (see Fig. 6.2(3)).

5 Protected shafts and protecting structures

In order to clarify the meaning of these two terms it is necessary to recall from Chapter 4, Section 5 that a 'protected shaft' includes stairways, lift shafts, shafts containing escalators, chutes, ducts and any other shaft enabling people, air or things to pass between compartments. The term also includes a shaft to accommodate pipes. It is, therefore, a void and not a structure, i.e. it is simply a space in which the stairs, lifts, etc. are placed. The term 'protecting structure' now probably becomes obvious: it is any wall or floor (or other elements of structure) enclosing such a shaft which when so enclosed becomes a 'protected shaft'. There are certain reservations to this general statement, however, and these are:

(i) A wall which forms part of an external wall, separating wall or compartment cannot also be controlled structurally as part of an enclosing protecting structure by regulation; in other words, any rules and supplementary instruction pertaining to their named function will always have priority.

(ii) A compartment floor retains its functional rules. A floor laid directly on the ground serves no protecting function, and so it is excepted.

(iii) A roof has no shaft protecting function, so this is also excepted.

These principles are illustrated in Fig. 7.3.

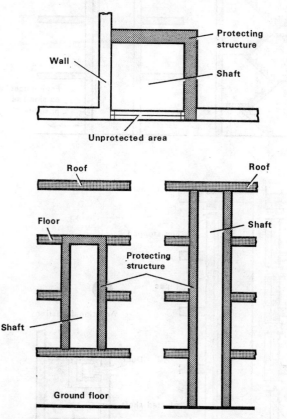

Fig. 7.3 Definition of enclosing surfaces of protected shafts which form a protecting structure.

As a general rule a protecting structure for which the Regulations require a fire resistance of 60 minutes or more, and any beam or column supporting such a structure, must have a Class O surface.

As sanitary accommodation is of low fire risk, it may be situated within a protected shaft.

121

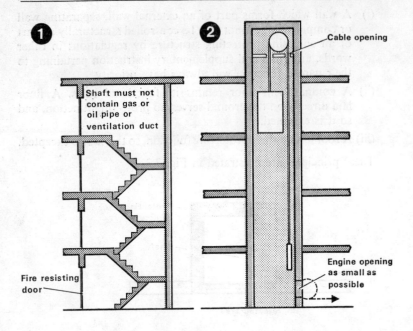

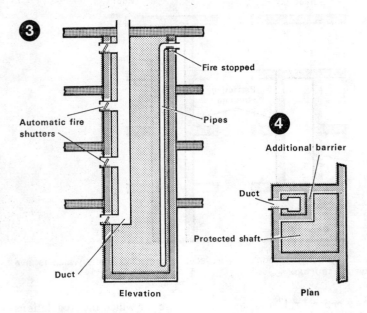

Fig. 7.4 Diagrams illustrating permitted openings in protected shafts. (1) Stairways; (2) lift shaft; (3 and 4) shaft containing vent duct. *Note:* Fire-resisting doors in residential (other than small dwelling houses), office and assembly buildings must provide 30 minutes fire resistance. In other cases they must provide half the resistance of the containing wall and never less than 30 minutes.

Plate 28. The traditional church building of solid construction.

Plate 29.   The interior of a traditional church showing the large open spaces, timber close-boarded roof and timber pews.

Plate 30. A modern church exterior used for multi purposes.

Plate 31. The interior of a modern church building which shows one of the multi-purpose uses. In this case a play school.

Plate 32.   An exterior view of a high bay warehouse showing the extent and size of this modern storage facility.

Plate 33.   An example of a town centre development.

Plate 34.   An air-supported structure showing the air-lock principle to facilitate easy access against the difference of pressures.

Plate 35. A multi-storey car park showing the open sides allowing heat and smoke to escape in case of fire.

Plate 36. An interior view of a multi-storey car park.

Plate 37. A typical installation of air recirculating units providing dust extraction for a panel production line in a kitchen furniture factory. Note in this photograph the modular nature of the system reduces the propagation of fire as compared with systems employing large centralised collectors.

Plate 38. A conventional cyclone dust separator with a two-way discharge. One feeds a rotary table silo which in turn delivers wood waste to the wood fired air heater automatically and combustion controlled by thermocouples. The other outlet will allow wooden chips to be diverted to an overflow should the silo become full, automatically controlled by a silo level switch. Reduced handling and uncontrolled storage lessens the fire risk.

6 Permitted openings in protected shafts

Certain openings into protected shafts are allowed by the Regulations. These vary according to the type of shaft involved. The three main types are: a stairway (Fig. 7.4(1)), a lift shaft (Fig. 7.4(2)) and a shaft containing a ventilation duct (Fig. 7.4(3 and 4)). Doors entering a shaft have never less than 30 minutes' fire resistance standard, and in some buildings they must provide half the fire resistance of the enclosing wall. Where a compartment wall forms part of the enclosure to the shaft, however, doors in the compartment wall may have to be of the full standard of the wall. This reduction for doors in protecting structure may appear to be a definite weakness, but as the object of protecting the shaft is to prevent the fire from spreading from floor to floor, the half-wall standard becomes justifiable in that, should a fire breach a door at one level and enter the shaft, it must also breach another door from the shaft side at a higher level (another half-wall standard door) to enter and endanger another compartment. In effect the two doors aggregate the full fire resistance standard of the containing wall.

7 Fire-resisting doors and other enclosures

Buildings divided into compartments must be provided with fire-resisting doors, shutters and occasionally floor hatches. These may occur in compartment walls, separating walls and protecting structures. The Regulations set out the standards of doors required in terms of fire resistance, the directions of openings and requisite self-closing devices.

Doors and frames in walls separating flats and maisonettes from common corridors, doors between houses and small garages, and doors in stairways of private residential premises of three storeys and over giving access to a habitable room or kitchen, are required to retain their stability for 30 minutes and integrity for 20 minutes. There is no requirement as to insulation. This type of door is referred to as a 'fire-check door' (see Fig. 5.31 on page 99).

It should be noted that doors in protected shafts and in compartment walls are only required to meet the standards of fire resistance (appropriate to their situation) in respect of stability and integrity; there is no requirement for insulation. The philosophy behind this is that, since a door is necessarily part of a thoroughfare, there will be open space on either side of it, and this means that combustible material will not be placed as to suffer exposure to radiated heat transmitted through the door. While this is acceptable in theory, there is little doubt that it can produce a hazard in some situations. Some doors may be no longer used for giving access, and as a consequence may have goods piled against them, such as in a warehouse or factory. This practice should be discouraged quite apart from any function the door may have in providing means of escape.

It is sometimes convenient to install two doors in an opening and in these cases it is sufficient for both doors together, or by either of the two doors separately, to have the required fire resistance specified in the Regulations.

Any door and frame other than those described above must satisfy BS 476 as to stability and integrity for the period prescribed in the Regulations for a particular use and must have the same fire resistance standard as the wall. Again, there is no requirement as to insulation on the assumption that combustible materials will not be placed dangerously close to them.

Many authorities allow existing doors to be converted to 30 minutes' fire-resisting standard by the infilling of the panels or covering a flush door with non-combustible material, such as asbestos wallboard or plasterboard. As the efficiency of a door as a fire check is also affected by its fit in the frame, the size of frame rebates, type of self-closing device and hinge specification, each conversion can only be allowed by the authority concerned dependent on all the circumstances. An example of a converted door is shown in Fig. 7.5.

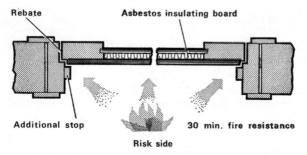

Fig. 7.5 A method of adapting a panelled door to 30 minutes' fire resistance standard.

8 Self-closing devices and hinges

Doors in new buildings (post 1965) are required (but see below) to be fitted with automatic self-closing devices (see Fig. 5.24 on page 94). This does not include rising butt hinges, except that these are permitted in doors separating flats and maisonettes from common areas, doors between houses and small garages and doors in stairways of private residential buildings. Fusible links are permitted and these usually relate to shutters or doors hung on an inclined track (see Fig. 5.27 on page 96). Any door in a protected shaft operated by a fusible link must be backed up with another door which closes automatically when, as previously stated, either or both doors together have the required fire resistance.

Hinges must be non-combustible with any part having a melting point of not less than 800°C. This rule precludes the use of plastic hinges or hinge pins which often fail very rapidly in fire conditions.

9 Automatic door releases

In certain circumstances, Building Regulations introduced in 1973 relax the previous requirements for self-closing doors to be fitted in such situations as doorways in compartment walls or in protecting structure. It is now permitted to attach to a self-closing door an automatic device (which may be electro-mechanical or electro-magnetic) (Fig. 7.6) whereby the door remains normally in the open position and is automatically released and returns to the closed

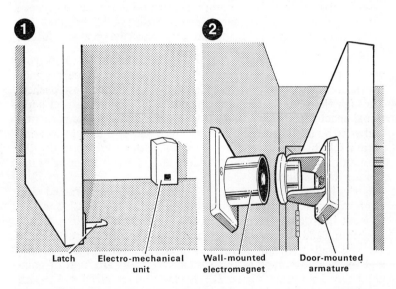

| Latch | Electro-mechanical unit | Wall-mounted electromagnet | Door-mounted armature |

Fig. 7.6 Automatic door releases. (1) Electro-mechanical type. (2) Electro-magnetic type.

position on the detection of the presence of smoke by a smoke detector associated with the door. Sometimes, the detection of smoke is part of a full detection system fitted in the building and not strictly associated with a particular door. Doors held open in this way are required to be released also by the actuation of a manual fire alarm if one is fitted in the building.

Chapter 8
Space separation

1 External walls

a. Protection from radiated heat

The fundamental principles of this aspect of fire protection were laid down in a proclamation by Charles II immediately following the Great Fire of London. This required:

> 'that the walls of all new buildings were to be of brick or stone: that the main streets were to be made so wide that fire could not cross from one side to the other (as it had done so easily between the overhanging upper storeys of the earlier buildings), and that the number of narrow lanes and alleys must be greatly reduced'.

This proclamation was followed by a Rebuilding Act; surveyors were appointed with other responsible officers to enforce the wide provisions of the Act. Building control thus became established. Through the years came many amendments, regulations and additional enactments which all dealt with brick and stone construction and were mainly concerned with the thickness of external walls and permissible heights. The criteria for the latter were generally the limitation of length of escape ladders and effective range of water jets for fire fighting.

Early in the 20th century, the concept of steel framed and reinforced concrete structures became a reality and legislation was brought in to control these then new methods of building. In the steel frame and reinforced concrete frame types of construction, the external walls need not contribute to the support of the structure, and to take advantage of this system, the walls are built of comparatively lightweight materials. Byelaws were introduced which required:

(i) an external wall to contain a fire within a building; and

(ii) the prevention of spread of fire *from* adjacent buildings;

(iii) the openings to prevent the spread of fire from storey to storey.

The byelaws did not control space around buildings, neither did they specify precisely the amount of permissible openings in external walls. There was, therefore, lack of clear interpretation of these requirements. The solid parts of the external wall were of fire-resisting construction, and the storey-to-storey spread factor was taken care of by the provision of not less than 3 ft (914 mm) of solid construction between the lintel of the lower window and the sill of the one above, of which at least 2 ft (610 mm) was above floor level. Where curtain walling was used, this feature was built into the structure as a partial second 'skin' and became known as a 'back-up' wall. Alternatively, a projection or balcony was used.

These requirements were based on the theory that flames issuing from a window opening are carried up the face of the building by convection currents and would not enter the windows on the floor above provided the solid 3 ft (914 mm) upstand was incorporated below the windows. Scientific investigation carried out in the 1950s, however, demonstrated that this theory was erroneous. It was shown that, according to circumstances, the flames, issuing from a lower storey might or might not ignite the contents of the room above by penetrating the window, but that the existence of a 3 ft (914 mm) upstand below the window did not materially affect the results. Following this research, the requirement for the upstand, which had been a feature of the Model Building Bye-Laws, was not perpetuated in the Building Regulations which superseded the former in 1966.

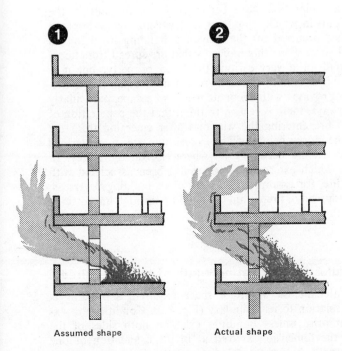

Assumed shape   Actual shape

Fig. 8.1 Diagrams showing the behaviour of flames emanating from an open window.

b. Current Building Regulations

In the light of these and other parallel experiments, a more logical approach was made to the problem, concentrating on the effects of heat radiated from one building on to the face of another. A new formula was developed which relates the amount of clear space between buildings and their boundaries to the amount of permissible openings in the face of the building. If a building is proposed some distance from its boundary, a considerable proportion (perhaps the whole) of the elevation may constitute 'unprotected area', and in this area no fire resistance is required at all. If the building is on or within 1 metre of the boundary, substantially the whole of the external wall facing that boundary is required to be fully fire resisting though there is always a small proportion of wall area that may be unprotected.

This is the position pertaining in the current Building Regulations. There are, of course, wide variations between the extremes of fully fire resisting and fully unprotected, and it follows that, as the distance between the external wall and the boundary increases, the amount of openings and combustible material on the wall can also be increased.

The effect of these new requirements for fire resistance in the external walls has been to leave alone the question of preventing fire spread by flame travel from storey to storey on the outside of buildings. Spectacular fires have occurred (not commonly in the United Kingdom) in which it appears that violent and widespread flame travel has occurred up the face of a building involving all floors in rapid succession; this indicates that fire spread from floor-to-floor externally is a very serious threat to property, but it is accepted that this does not necessarily represent an equal risk to life. If a building is provided with adequate means of escape, particularly protected stairways, there is reason to think that the penetration of the storeys by fire entering the windows after emerging from the windows on the storey below will not constitute any more serious life hazard than a fire occurring anywhere else on the storey. In those cases in which external fire travel has been associated with heavy loss of life, for example, in certain office buildings overseas, there has been spread of fire within the building through unprotected openings, which has constituted the real cause of loss of life.

c. General rules for calculating width of space required

In order to calculate the width of space required, a building is considered in relation to its boundary (Fig. 8.2). Conditions of exposure do not arise unless buildings exist on both sides of the boundary, so the dimension arrived at in the calculation of one building is actually half the total distance which would separate two similar buildings.

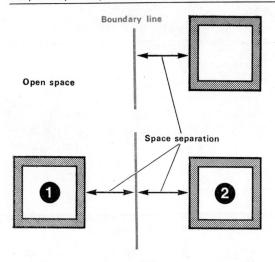

Fig. 8.2 The total space between two similar buildings is calculated by taking the distance from each building to its boundary.

d. Limitation of permitted openings

The amount of permitted openings in an external wall depends on:

   (i) the use to which the building is to be put;

   (ii) the distance of the building from its boundary.

An external wall on or near the boundary must be virtually imperforate (Fig. 8.3(1)), but the farther from the boundary the

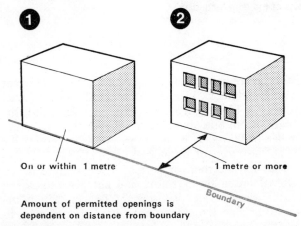

Fig. 8.3 The limitation of permitted openings in an external wall. (1) A building on or within 1 metre of the boundary; (2) a building 1 metre or more from the boundary.

building is erected – and hence the less the degree of exposure hazard to its neighbour – the greater the amount of openings which are permitted (Fig. 8.3(2)).

e. The boundary

The definition of the term 'boundary' is the boundary of the land belonging to the building (Fig. 8.4) and is taken to include the centre line of any adjacent part of a street, canal or river. A separating wall is considered to be a boundary.

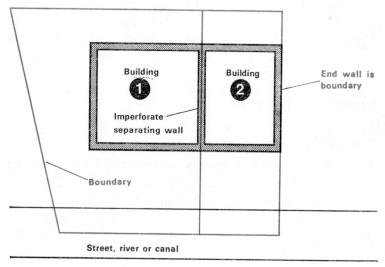

Fig. 8.4 Examples of the term 'boundary'.

2 Roofs

Requirements for the fire protection of roofs are somewhat different from those for walls and floors. Like the external wall, the roof must in all cases protect the building from exposure hazard; against the risk of flying brands from other buildings on fire, or from radiation from nearby taller buildings. It is, however, not so necessary for roofs to withstand the effects of an internal fire; indeed, it is sometimes advantageous for the roof, or part of it, to collapse in the event of an internal fire, allowing smoke and hot gases to escape which would otherwise impede the work of firemen within the building. On the other hand, a roof must not cause serious damage to the remainder of the building in the event of its collapse. A heavy, reinforced roof, for example, could cause further collapse lower down in the building.

In general, therefore, roofs are constructed of comparatively lightweight materials. The Building Regulations require a certain designation in respect of both the time of penetration of external fire and the spread of flame along its external surface. Details of these requirements have been explained in Chapter 5, Section 2, 'Roofs'.

Chapter 9
Building construction methods

Before passing on to a study of the various types of building and considering examples of each, it is necessary for the fireman to have some knowledge of the principal methods used in building construction and to appreciate the concept of the grading of buildings by the use or the occupancy to which they are put. In the fire service a system has been adopted for classifying the various types of building construction, particularly for the purpose of completing the fire report form (K.433). This chapter will deal with the constructional methods employed in buildings and will give examples of the various classifications of construction for the reporting of fires in buildings before passing on, in Chapter 10, to a description of various types of building according to their use or occupancy.

1 Constructional methods

Having considered the various types of material used in elements of structure, the principal systems used in the construction of buildings will now be discussed. The fireman is also, from time to time, called upon to rescue persons trapped in buildings which have collapsed for reasons other than the effects of fire. A knowledge of which portions can safely be shifted and those which would be dangerous to move is, in such circumstances, essential.

a. Solid construction
Solid construction (Fig. 9.1), which is also referred to as traditional or masonry construction, consists of loadbearing external walls which support the floors and roof. The materials most commonly used are brick, concrete blocks and stone, although the latter is now primarily used as a facing rather than a structural material.

This form of construction was almost universal during the 19th century and before for all kinds of industrial and commercial buildings, but for multi-storey buildings this has now been superseded by framed construction (see below). The example shown in Fig. 9.1 is a warehouse, but factories, office buildings, cotton and woollen mills were all similarly constructed.

The walls are of solid brick or stone 1 metre or more thick at the bottom but setting back on the upper floors. Cast-iron columns support either cast iron or wooden beams which are bedded in the load-bearing walls at either end. With timber beams the commonest

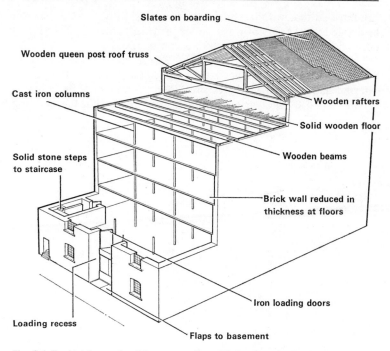

Slates on boarding

Wooden queen post roof truss

Cast iron columns

Wooden rafters

Solid wooden floor

Wooden beams

Solid stone steps
to staircase

Brick wall reduced in
thickness at floors

Iron loading doors

Loading recess

Flaps to basement

Fig. 9.1 Typical form of solid construction with loadbearing walls used during the 19th century for large buildings such as mills, warehouses, etc.

type of floor is of 50 to 75 mm solid wooden boarding spanning from beam to beam. Many of the older buildings (in which cast-iron beams are used) have barrel vaults and a few of the later ones have concrete floors on steel filler joists. The commonest roof is a slated pitched roof on wooden rafters, purlins and supported by roof trusses.

b. Structural steel frame construction

The modern framed building was first evolved in America in the form of the skyscraper. It was found that to erect a building of more than eight or ten floors with load-bearing walls, the walls had to be so thick to carry the weight of the structure that they became extremely expensive, and interfered with the planning and lighting of the building. The use of steel framing to carry the weight of the building meant that the walls could be reduced in thickness to the minimum necessary to keep out the weather and insulate the building. Steel-framed buildings over 305 metres high have been built.

The great advantage from the designer's point of view is that in this type of construction the loads of the floors and cladding are carried at each level by beams which in turn pass the loads on to the columns, so that within a skeleton framework, floor space that can be divided in a variety of ways can be provided, and one of the many non-load-bearing cladding materials can be used.

The skeleton of the building (Fig. 9.2) is made up of universal beams and columns designed to support the loads of the floors, external cladding and wind pressure. The arrangement of the columns is determined by the various circulation spaces within the building

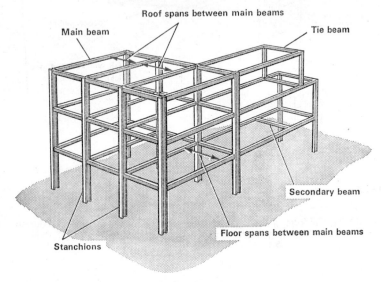

Fig. 9.2 An example of a structural steel frame for a building.

and to some extent the window openings. The typical arrangement of beams and columns shown in Fig. 9.2 has columns 3·6 metres apart and floor beams spanning 6 metres. This allows the smallest (and the most economical) thickness of floor slab consistent with the fire resistance requirements of any particular building. The steel-work would be required to be protected against fire by either 'solid' or 'hollow' protection (see page 44).

This rectangular grid system can be extended in both directions. Where large floor areas are required to be unobstructed by columns, deep long span open web or latticed beams (Fig. 9.3) are used.

c. Reinforced concrete construction

The reinforced concrete frame (Fig. 9.4) constructed immediately after the Second World War were treated as an alternative for steel frames, i.e. the columns supported the main beams which in turn supported the floor slabs. Some systems still employ this concept.

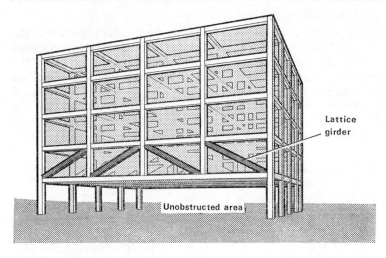

Fig. 9.3 Example of lattice girder supporting the frame above to provide an unobstructed open area.

It was soon learned, however, that a design in which the beams are rigidly attached to the columns, and the floors are cast integrally with the beams, made for a stronger and more economic building. This monolithic type of structure is often called 'slab construction' although 'slab' really only refers to the type of floor used.

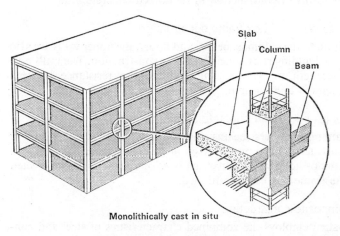

Fig. 9.4 In situ reinforced concrete frame type of construction.

(1) Lift slab construction

In another type of reinforced concrete construction, known as the 'lift slab' system (Plate 20) the columns are progressively extended and the floor slabs are cast on site around them, one on top of the other (Fig. 9.5). The roof slab and upper storey floor slabs are raised by jacks and 'parked' on the columns whilst the lower floor slabs are fixed into their correct positions. As building progresses and the columns are extended, the process is repeated until the roof and all the floor slabs are in place (Plate 21).

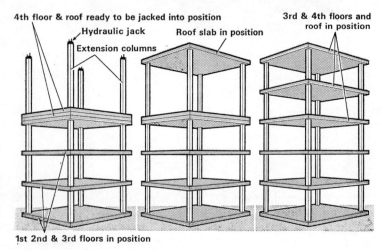

Fig. 9.5 Diagrams showing the 'lift slab' type of construction.

Other forms of construction in reinforced concrete are:

(2) Cross wall and box frame construction

In addition to the columns, beams and floors, the upper walls are also cast as the building rises in height during construction. The walls give added strength to the building and the fire resistance between occupancies is thus assured.

(3) Precast reinforced concrete frame

The framing members, beams and columns are made at a factory and constructed in a similar fashion to steel frame construction. The floors of hollow tile, concrete plank or similar form are erected after the frame has been positioned.

(4) Composite construction

This system employs the combined characteristics of steel and concrete.

(5) Other types of structure

Reinforced concrete lends itself to many forms of structure, limited possibly only by the complexity of the casting moulds (formwork). A great deal of research and experimental work is being carried out with this material and the forms of structure and methods of construction will vary as new knowledge is gained.

d. Portal frame construction

In the Portal frame type of construction (Fig. 9.6), which is mostly used for single storey structures, the concrete, steel or timber columns are rigidly connected to the structural roof members (Plate 22). The structural continuity of the frame, which seldom needs bracing within, results in a large unencumbered working or storage space. The roof covering is supported by concrete, steel or timber secondary members (purlins).

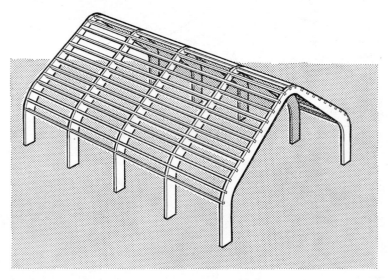

Fig. 9.6 Diagram of a laminated timber Portal frame for a building.

e. Lightweight steel construction

In this type of construction (Fig. 9.7), open-web steel joists are used. These are lightweight steel trusses suitable for the direct support of floors and roof decks. The joists are positioned either on structural steel framing or on loadbearing masonry walls. It will be seen from Fig. 9.8 that open-joist construction allows space for electrical systems, ducts and piping between the ceiling and the underside of the floor above. They are made in depths of from 200 mm to 610 mm.

137

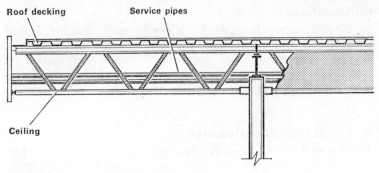

Fig. 9.7 An example of lightweight steel construction.

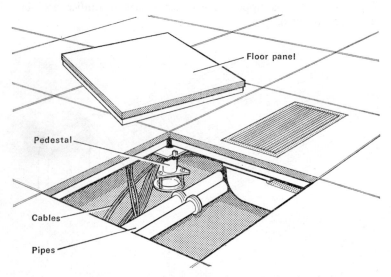

Fig. 9.8 Lightweight steel construction allowing space for electrical systems, ducts, etc.

f. Timber construction

Timber construction to modern techniques can be strong and durable and is generally lower in cost than concrete or steel. Heavy timber construction will often withstand fire better than unprotected steel construction. Timber, however, is combustible and its use as structural framing is limited to dwelling houses, farm buildings, temporary classrooms and offices, sports pavilions and single storey community buildings. It should be noted that in many buildings, glue laminated structural members are displacing the traditional solid timber members often because, among other things, the latter are not commercially available in the longer lengths. Laminated timber Portal frames have been used in this country for about twenty years and many designs are available which would not be possible with other materials. Fig. 9.9 shows a variety of shapes currently used.

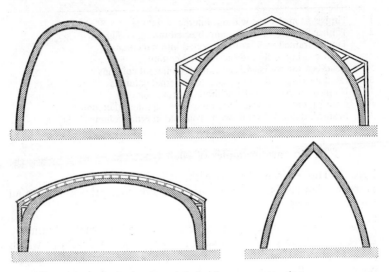

Fig. 9.9 Examples of glue laminated timber frame construction.

g. Modular design construction

Modular measure is a simplified unit or standard size system which enables designers to co-ordinate the building layout dimensions with stock unit sizes of building materials. It is the building industry's counterpart of the production line in, say, engineering manufacturing. Building products are standardised in size so that they can be readily fitted together and when assembled form a complete structure. Other terms used for modular construction are 'industrial building systems' and 'prefabrication'.

2 Types of building construction

The various types of building construction can conveniently be described by the use of a 'type number' which relates to the basic type of construction and which is amplified as necessary to include the number of basements and storeys, the types of floor construction, the type of roof and the type of wall. This system is used in Great Britain for the reporting of fires for statistical analysis. Table 4 sets out the basic types of construction.

Table 4
Types of building construction

No.	Building construction
1	Timber-framed walls without internal columns
2	Timber-framed walls with unprotected internal columns
3	Timber-framed walls with protected internal columns
4	Load-bearing walls without internal columns
5	Load-bearing walls with unprotected internal columns
6	Load-bearing walls with protected internal columns
7	Framed, unloaded walls, without internal columns
8	Framed, unloaded walls, with unprotected internal columns
9	Framed, unloaded walls, with protected internal columns

The following are examples of each type:

Type 1: Timber-framed walls without internal columns:
Huts, garden sheds, summerhouses, seaside 'bungalows' and small sports pavilions.

Type 2: Timber-framed walls with unprotected internal columns:
Large single storey buildings such as garages and workshops which have internal columns and of which the walls consist of weatherboarding, or flat or corrugated sheets on a timber framework.

Type 3: Timber-framed walls with protected internal columns:
This type of construction is comparatively rare; it is similar to type 2, but the internal columns are protected by a casing of fire-resisting material.

Type 4: Load-bearing walls without internal columns:
Almost all residential houses, many old office buildings, public houses, older type hotels and hospitals, small shops and churches without pillars are of this type of construction.

Type 5: Load-bearing walls with unprotected internal columns:
This type includes old single-storey factory or storage buildings of multiple span, in which the internal columns are timber posts or unencased iron or steel; old mill buildings with brick or stone walls and cast-iron columns; old warehouses with timber posts supporting the floors, and many large railway stations.

Type 6: Load-bearing walls with protected internal columns:
Many large old office buildings, departmental stores, churches and cathedrals with pillared aisles are in this category. (The pillars are not strictly protected internal columns but are inherently fire-resisting – see 'elements of structure'.)

Type 7: Framed, unloaded walls without internal columns:
Single-span sheeted buildings, e.g. medium-sized garages and aircraft hangars; many cinemas are also in this class.

Type 8: Framed, unloaded walls with unprotected internal columns: This category covers large single storey steel factory and storage buildings and some departmental stores. Columns in many of the older departmental stores are encased in decorative timberwork which conceals the unprotected metal column.

Type 9: Framed, unloaded walls with protected internal columns: In this category are multi-storey office buildings, high blocks of flats and maisonettes, some multi-storey car parks and modern departmental stores.

3 Standards of construction for insurance purposes

Fire Insurance interests use standards of construction which have been compiled over a number of years from the collated experience of insurers and from tests of the performance of materials and elements of structure by the Fire Research Station and other testing laboratories. These standards differ somewhat from current Building Regulations (which are minimum standards) and relate to the fire risk inherent in the buildings to be insured.

It is not considered appropriate to set out in full the various standards, but firemen should be aware of their existence and should know that they range from Standard I: buildings having a very high degree of fire resistance, to Standard V: the minimum constructural standard. Fire insurance surveyors assess the standard and the insurance premium is calculated in terms of fire risk both in respect of the building and its contents.

Chapter 10
Examples of buildings

In the Building Regulations the purposes for which buildings are used (or intended to be used in the case of proposed buildings) are divided into designations called 'purpose' or 'occupancy' groups. These groupings reflect the potential hazard that is expected to exist in relation to both the fire load (i.e. the amount of combustible material) and to the safety of the persons likely to be within the buildings should a fire occur. At the top end of the groupings are residential and institutional-use buildings which have a sleeping risk – in certain cases worsened by the fact that some occupants would have difficulty of movement without assistance – through the scale to buildings used for storage wherein the fire damage potential might be high but the life risk comparatively low. Personal safety has, nevertheless, been taken into account in all groupings.

Amongst other things, the Regulations limit the size of a building in relation to the period of fire resistance of its elements of structure (see Chapter 4). Having determined the potential hazard of the use of the building, the Regulations ensure that it has sufficient fire resistance to prevent a major collapse or lead to a large-scale spread of fire.

Examples of buildings will be studied, mainly by illustration, according to these groupings. There are various types of construction within each of the groups and only a representative selection is made. The Regulations apply only to:

(i)   new buildings;
(ii) structural alterations or extensions to existing buildings (irrespective of when the building was erected);
(iii) to certain works or fittings (including replacements), e.g. drains, incinerators, etc.;
(iv) when a material change of use is deemed to have been proposed.

Firemen will, therefore, still have to consider buildings erected before the introduction of the Building Regulations, which are often sub-standard compared with those erected under current building practice. Examples are given in many cases of 'old' and 'new' buildings used for similar purposes.

1 Residential buildings

For the purpose of the Building Regulations, residential buildings are sub-divided into small residential, such as private dwelling houses, and other residential, which includes flats, maisonettes, hotels and hostels. Varying building regulations apply depending upon which sub-group a residential building is placed when application is made to the building authority to erect the building.

a. Half-timbered private houses

The oldest type of domestic architecture in anything like general use today is the half-timbered house of which, apart from those in country districts, a large number still stand closely crowded together in the centres of old towns where they form a fire risk out of all proportion to their size and the value of their contents. The walls are built of a framework of heavy oak posts, tenoned and pegged to oak sills at the top and bottom. The space between the posts is filled-in either with plaster on a backing of laths, or with brickwork.

The upper floor beams are often cantilevered out from the face of the building so that each floor projects over the one below. The weight of each floor is thus balanced see-saw fashion by the weight of the wall. Contrary to expectations, these cantilevered walls are surprisingly stable in a fire and complete collapses are infrequent, but the brick nogging may come away. Although the heavy oak posts and beams are very fire resistant, and even the smaller oak floor beams and boarding are often more resistant than modern softwood flooring, the many concealed spaces, the labyrinthine passages and the considerable alterations and additions carried out through the centuries make them extremely vulnerable and fire usually spreads with great speed.

Reconditioning and modernising of these buildings has often still further increased the fire risk. Roof coverings may be of tile but are very often of thatch sometimes up to 1 metre thick.

b. Terrace and semi-detached houses

The old type of terrace housing has the outer walls and separating walls of brick or stone and the internal walls either of brick or, more commonly, framed with wooden studs faced each side with lath and plaster. These wooden internal walls often carry part of the weight of the floors which span between them and either the outer or separating walls. The wooden floor joists have boarding on top and lath and plaster or plaster board ceilings underneath. The roof is wood and has a tiled, slated or sometimes sheet lead (or zinc) covering. Virtually the whole of the inside structure is thus of timber and fires in this type of building may, unless properly handled, result in a complete burn-out, leaving only the brick or stone shell. In many larger terrace houses there are cross walls of brickwork to support the floors, though these do not prevent the building being gutted if a fire gets away.

This type of building is often sub-divided into flats and tenements, and the resulting overcrowding enormously increases the risk. The means of escape are often inadequate for the new circumstances, and there may be difficulty in gaining access to the rear of the building in a long terrace.

The separating walls in terrace houses of old construction may only be carried up to the ceiling of the top floor, and not to the underside of the slates or tiles. The roof space is thus continuous along the whole terrace, and fire can spread easily from house to house. The Building Regulations now require separating walls to be carried up through the roof to at least 375 mm above the roof unless other precautions are taken, such as using non-combustible or highly-rated fire-resistant roofing materials within 1·5 metres of the wall, and also that other limitations are complied with to ensure that fire cannot spread over the top of the wall.

c. Pre-fabricated buildings

In the immediate post-war years, in order to meet the acute housing shortage, various proprietary building systems were used to construct pre-fabricated houses (known as 'prefabs'). The intention at that time was that the life span of this type of construction would be extremely short compared with a traditional type dwelling. Now, almost 30 years later, many of these dwellings are still carrying out the function for which they were designed. This type of construction was the forerunner of modular design systems.

d. Flats and maisonettes

For all practical purposes the term 'flat' means 'a dwelling, forming part of a larger block with common access, which has all its habitable rooms and kitchen on one level, or, in the case of 'split-level flats', not more than half-a-storey apart'. It has been stated in (b) above that terrace and semi-detached houses are often converted to flats which bring added hazards to the building and its occupants. Purpose-built flats, however, are generally more than two storeys and are referred to as multi-storey, high point or tower blocks.

A maisonette differs from a flat in that, although it forms part of a larger block with common access, its habitable rooms and kitchen are divided between two or more levels which are more than half a storey in height apart.

The protection of the occupants from fire, and their ways of escape from the building is one of the fundamental design principles in the planning of multi-storey blocks. The concept of using fire brigade ladders has long gone. Non-combustible construction and the protection of escape routes from fire spread are the important factors.

It is no longer assumed that when a fire occurs in a block of flats or maisonettes, it is necessary to evacuate the whole block or even dwellings adjacent to the fire, The fire resistance between dwellings must, therefore, be substantial. There must be no risk from fire in the escape corridors, staircases or common entrance halls. Limits are set on how far a person must travel to the normal entrance door of the dwelling or alternative escape if provided, and to the accepted place of safety which will generally be a lobby leading to a main staircase or to a balcony (Fig. 10.1).

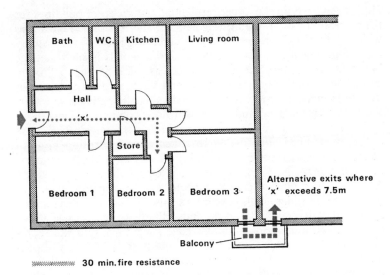

Fig. 10.1 Plan of a tower block flat showing a linking balcony as a means of escape.

The route from the staircase to the external door at ground or podium level is regarded as an extension of the staircase and is protected accordingly.

Many design arrangements of maisonettes are possible. They vary from the most common type (Fig. 10.2), which is approached from a common open balcony or deck, with living rooms at entrance level and bedrooms over on the floor above, to complex cross-over

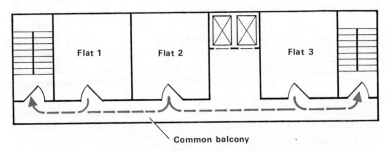

Fig. 10.2 Layout showing a number of maisonettes with a common balcony escape route to staircases at the end.

interlocking forms extending through two or more floors with living rooms, kitchens and bedrooms on any floor. As with flats, the escape arrangements are designed into the building.

e. Hotels

Hotels come within the 'other residential' use group of buildings for the purposes of the Building Regulations, and it is these regulations which limit the floor area and the cubic capacity of each storey (or compartment). In general, the design of hotels is such that the lower floors contain the amenities areas such as the ballroom, conference rooms, bars, restaurants and kitchens, whilst the upper floors are given over to bedrooms and suites. Sometimes, however, the pattern is changed and a topmost floor contains a dance floor and restaurant – a 'roof room' as they are often called. The floors containing the bedrooms are compartmented with corridors of up to 36 metres, the bedroom doors opening directly on to these corridors. A small pantry and a linen room are often provided on each floor. A typical floor plan of a modern hotel is shown in Fig. 10.3.

Many of the older hotels have been so altered and extended that the system of stairs, corridors, dead ends, difference in levels of floors and confused numbering of rooms have made them into such complex buildings that a guest could become 'lost', which in fire conditions could be fatal. Only comparatively recently have real efforts been made to rationalise this type of structure by providing alternative means of escape, directional signs, emergency lighting, alarm systems and fire extinguishing equipment. The *Fire Precautions Act 1971* was designed to enable fire authorities to insist upon reasonable measures being taken in hotels (and other premises) to protect the persons staying in the premises by assuring that they can escape from fire safely and quickly. Plates 23 and 24 show typical old and new hotels.

2 Institutional buildings

This designation includes buildings which are used as hospitals, homes, schools and similar establishments where persons in need of treatment or care sleep on the premises. No single specific form of construction is used for buildings in this group, and they are to be found as converted country mansions, old Victorian-type cast-iron and stone structures, single-storey modular unit type buildings and modern steel-framed, multi-storey buildings. The Building Regulations recognise the life risk in premises in this use category and require new and converted buildings to have substantial fire-resisting compartmentation, and also limit the floor area of each storey in the compartment of which the floor forms part.

The Government Departments responsible for hospitals and other Crown properties of the nursing and care type have made concerted

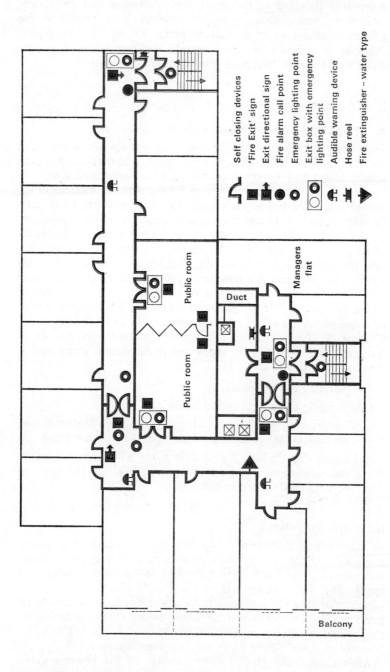

Fig. 10.3 Floor plan of a modern hotel.

147

efforts over the past few years to bring the older buildings up to an acceptable standard in respect of fire prevention and protection, and many management group committees have appointed fire officers to advise on these matters. Plates 25 and 26 show typical examples of old and modern hospitals. References should also be made to Section 9, 'Hospital development' on page 159.

3 Commercial buildings

a. Shops and departmental stores

The variety of building forms for shops and stores is almost unlimited and ranges from single-storey shops, through extensive open-plan supermarkets and hypermarkets to huge departmental stores. In the first there is little or no problem for the fireman, whereas in the second and third types, tremendous fire problems arise, especially in older properties. In recent years the recognition of these problems has led to the *Offices, Shops and Railway Premises Act 1963*, which often enables fire authorities to require fire protection to be built into the structure. In new buildings which are known to be constructed for shop use, Building Regulations apply and, among other things, aim to restrict the extent of floor area and cubic capacity of the building and/or compartment within the building other than in single-storey buildings. *British Standard Code of Practice CP3, Chapter IV, Part 2 (1968)*, offers design guidance in respect of 'precautions against fire' in shops and departmental stores and is directed towards the safety of life by:

(i) planning escape routes;

(ii) planning to prevent spread of fire;

(iii) constructing and finishing with non-hazardous materials, and embodying adequate fire resistance in the structure; and

(iv) segregating the high risk areas (e.g. the selling area) from the non-selling area – stores, loading bays, receiving and despatch departments and other risk areas.

b. Projecting shops

In many towns, houses in terrace formation have, as development proceeded and the town spread outwards, been converted into shops, very often by building a section forward of the main frontage into the garden. This extension is normally only of one storey and is surmounted by a flat roof usually having one or more lantern lights (see Plate 27). This form of construction presents many difficulties to the fireman, which are discussed in the *Manual, Part 6A: Chapter 2*, 'Control at a fire' (Book 11 in the new format).

Alternatively, the ground floor frontage of the house may be removed and a large window substituted. In order to do this it is necessary to carry the weight of the wall above on a steel joist and as this is frequently not suitably encased to protect it from a fire (Fig. 10.4), its failure in a fire would lead to the collapse of the entire frontage of the building.

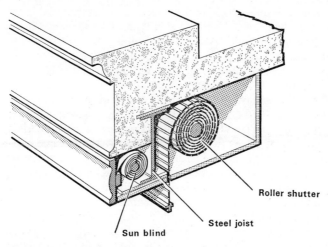

Fig. 10.4 Details of the arrangement of a steel joist over a shop window, showing wooden casing which also conceals the sunblind and roller shutter.

c. Office buildings and premises

There is no distinct form of building for this purpose and office premises may be situated in anything from a small single-storey 'cabin' type building to a multi-storey complex of buildings which often have occupancies other than offices within them, bringing added difficulties for the fire fighter.

Design guidance for new office buildings is given in *British Standard CP3, Chapter IV, Part 3 (1968)*. Sometimes the sub-division of floors of new offices is carried out after the erection of the building when the requirements of the lessees become known to the developers. In many cases the proposed sub-division must be approved by the appropriate authority as a condition of the grant of permission to build, but this is not so in every case and the fireman must be prepared for alterations to the layout of floors from time to time possibly without the fire brigade being notified.

4 Industrial buildings

a. General

Early purpose-built factories were constructed from comparatively easily obtained local materials. In many places, chiefly in the north of the country, this was stone and timber. There are still industrial buildings with load-bearing walls of predominantly random stone and brick, some of which are 1 metre or more thick at ground level, gradually tapering back to eaves level following the principle of the 'middle third' loading. Cast-iron or timber columns are used to support the floor beams which, in turn, support the substantial joists and thick floor boarding. Although this type of building is shown under the heading of 'industrial buildings' many are still in use as warehouses and for other purposes. A typical form of construction of 19th century building used as factory, mill or warehouse is shown in Fig. 9.1 on page 133.

It is common nowadays to find that the design of industrial buildings takes account of the processes to be carried on within them; most industrial layouts show an identifiable pattern of raw materials arriving at points of access from roads or railway sidings, and progressing round or through the factory, steadily taking the shape of finished products as the parts travel round the factory, ending at a finished goods store and a despatch department, the latter of which being again at an access point to the outside. In some industries this can be a top to ground movement, and in others, a continuous flow or belt-line system on ground-floor level only. Industrial buildings are found in any of the types of construction listed in Table 4 (page 140), the majority being purpose-built and others in premises constructed for an entirely different purpose. A building originally designed as a church or chapel, for example, could become an industrial premises in which, possibly, a highly hazardous process is carried on. Firemen must, therefore, gain practical knowledge of their station's ground in order to guard against the unexpected in these changing circumstances.

A characteristic of multi-storey industrial buildings (other than 'flatted factories', which are referred to below) is that openings are frequently required between storeys. These are needed to accommodate forms of power transmission, chutes, ducts and other means of conveying goods and even conveyor systems themselves from one floor to another. This produces substantial hazards of fire travel through the openings. The same applies, of course, to walls between workshops on the same floor, many of which are penetrated by openings of various sizes for drive shafts, etc. to pass through. The principal danger in this type of opening, which is not as evident as a doorway, for instance, is that they may be concealed or overlooked.

b. Single-storey factories

Many industrial processes, particularly in engineering, lend themselves to a conveyor belt system of production in which a part of the assembly or process is carried out before passing to the next operative who in turn carries out another portion of the assembly, and so on until the finished product is assembled (Fig. 10.5). Most of the factories adopting this technique of production require huge covered areas, as for example, vehicle manufacturing. Within these areas are certain high fire hazards, such as spray shops, flammable goods stores, etc., which are segregated from the main factory area by suitable fire-resisting materials.

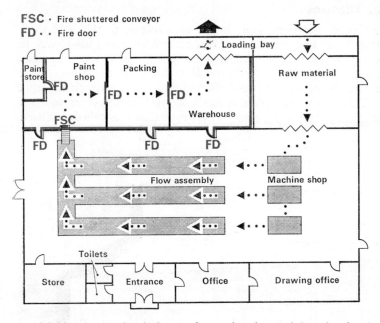

Fig. 10.5 Diagram showing the layout of an engineering workshop showing the assembly lines.

c. Flatted factories

A type of multi-storey industrial building which was popular before and after World War II was the 'flatted factory' which comprised a number of different industrial occupancies in the same building, the floors being imperforate and fire resisting, and the means of escape and access being common to all occupancies.

5 Public assembly buildings

This group comprises, amongst others, theatres, cinemas, concert halls, dance halls, museums, art galleries, churches, schools, non-residential clubs and bingo halls. Many of the premises coming within this category are within the scope of legislation and in these cases the fire authority has a responsibility in respect of fire precautions and means of escape. The *Fire Precautions Act 1971* will

151

progressively bring into its scope all premises used by the public for social, recreational and educational purposes. Buildings in this group are constructed in many forms. Examples of typical assembly buildings are shown.

a. Theatres

Reference has been made in the introduction to this Part to the traditional type of theatre building and its association with the development of compartmentation for fire separation purposes. As this illustrates a fundamental principle of the prevention of spread of fire, a close examination of this type of building is merited.

The traditional theatre consists of a substantial outer wall and, internally the seating area or auditorium, as it is called, is divided

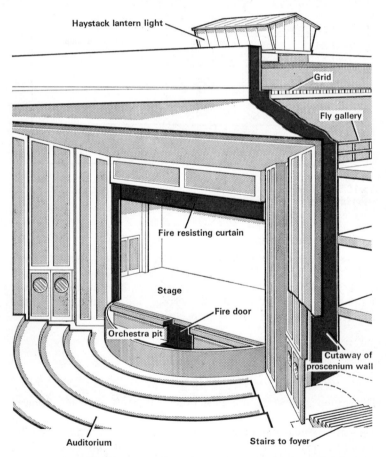

Fig. 10.6 Diagram of a traditional small stage theatre showing separation between auditorium and stage area.

into separate part floors at varying levels (circles) each having sufficient exits leading to protected staircases and to the safety of the open air. Between the auditorium and the stage is the proscenium opening (Figs. 10.6 and 10.7). Scenery in the form of painted fabrics, various types of curtain and other large pieces of material are stored

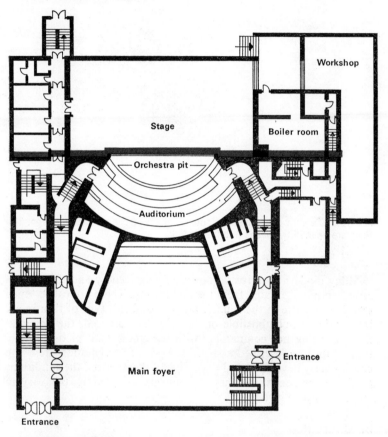

Fig. 10.7 Plan of the auditorium and stage area of the theatre shown in Fig. 10.6.

high over the stage, some on rollers in the hanging loft or 'fly gallery', so called because such scenic effects are termed 'flown or flying scenery'. Also in the stage area are the electronic and electrical controls for lighting, and sound and other set properties ('props') which are moved into the stage area from the scene dock as required.

As can be imagined, the fire risk in the stage area is considerable, so the stage area is isolated from the auditorium by a substantial wall (the proscenium wall). The opening in the wall (the stage

153

opening) is protected by a fire-resisting curtain (known as the 'iron') and this is further protected by the curtain drencher system. Roof ventilators in the form of haystack lantern lights (Fig. 10.8) are installed over the stage area for the rapid clearance of smoke.

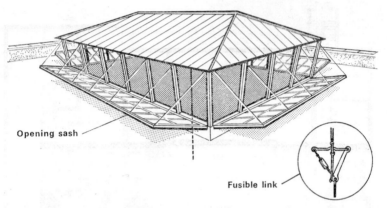

Fig. 10.8 Diagram of a haystack lantern light protecting a theatre stage. The sides are opened by means of a fusible link.

Many modern theatres do not use flying scenery and their stages are often not separated from the auditorium. These are called 'open stage' or 'theatre in the round'. Stage sets in this type of theatre are inherently non-combustible or durably flameproofed, the potential fire risk being not comparable with the traditional 'picture frame' type of theatre described above. Methods of presentation are being continuously developed and the design of theatres and the conditions of licence under which they operate are adapted to the varying methods of production.

b. Churches

The majority of churches are usually of solid construction (see Plate 28) often without fire and smoke separation. Very often they have large open areas with structural and decorative woodwork and timber pews (Plate 29) which could become involved in fire possibly affecting the whole of an unsupervised building. Some of the contents are irreplaceable; precious carvings, screens and stained glass are particularly vulnerable in fire, so also is the organ, the loft of which is often of timber construction which has become as dry as tinder in the course of time. The spire or tower, too, often connects with roof timbers and wooden ceilings, assisting the spread of fire and generally being most difficult of access for the fireman, making what appears at first sight to be a comparatively safe building a potentially high fire hazard. The life hazard in churches is, however, virtually non-existent. Fortunately, many church authorities have now recognised the fire risk and take effective fire prevention and protection measures to minimise it. Nevertheless, this type of building is a good example for study as it illustrates that the fireman can never afford to be complacent when assessing the risk of any type of structure.

Some modern church buildings (see Plates 30 and 31) are designed to be used as multi-purpose halls. The altar is screened off when the building is not being used as a place of worship, and activities take place quite remote from those normally expected. Dances, youth clubs and many other public assembly activities are usual with the result that they can be a life risk as in other buildings of public resort.

c. Educational buildings

This term covers a very wide range of buildings from the small village school to the largest complex of university buildings. These buildings are at present exempted from the Building Regulations, though not all are exempt from the Inner London legislation. Building control is vested with the Minister of Education and Science to whom plans for school buildings are submitted for approval. Guidance in respect of fire precautions is given in *Building Bulletin No. 7* for new primary and secondary day schools. Many boarding schools are subject to inspection by the Department of Education and Science for suitability and standards; fire brigade inspecting officers are often requested to report on the fire precautions aspect of such schools.

Many local authorities have co-operated in the design of a modular system of school building and often these systems are referred to by the name formed from the initial letters of the design group concerned; for example CLASP from Consortium Local Authorities Schools Programme, and SCOLA from Second Consortia of Local Authorities. The precautions set out in *Building Bulletin No. 7* are adhered to in these and other building systems and they are framed to permit the maximum freedom in planning compatible with ensuring personal safety. It should be noted that the CLASP and SCOLA systems whilst originally intended as a 'crash schools building programme' after the Second World War are now being used for many other types of occupancy.

6 Storage buildings

In this group are included warehouses, cold stores, spirit storages, garages used only for the storage or parking of vehicles and multi-storey car parks. All types of construction are used for this purpose group. The Building Regulations require a high standard of fire resistance in storage buildings relative to the size and siting of the building as the fire loading is comparatively much greater than for buildings in the other groups. The building has to be safeguarded against possible collapse and also against the spread of fire to adjacent property.

A description of the characteristics of buildings used as cold stores, together with their associated refrigeration machinery and hazards is given in the *Manual, Part 6C: Section 12, 'Refrigeration plant risks'* (Book 15 in the new format).

A particular example of storage building to which special considerations apply is the whisky storage warehouse. Following a disastrous fire and explosion in Glasgow in 1961, guidance has been issued by the Home Office on new single storey buildings used for spirit storage in Fire Prevention Guide No. 2. Notable features of construction recommended for these buildings are: limitation of compartment size; light roof construction to vent a possible explosion; the installation of a sprinkler system; restrictions on the height of racking; and specific amounts of natural ventilation.

7 Farm buildings

Farm buildings are divided into two main categories: (a) buildings which house livestock and (b) storage buildings.

In many cases they are designed so that structurally they are capable of being used for either purpose. The walls of stockhouses are usually of 228 mm brickwork to at least a height of 1·37 metres with sheeting, such as asbestos cement, above this height. Floors of stables and cowhouses are normally concrete with a rough non-slip finish. The contents in general present little fire hazard, although in modern farming, a considerable number of electrical appliances, semi-automatic feeding and milking machines bring in fire problems which equate with an industrial building in many cases.

Storage buildings for grain are approximately 5 metres to the eaves and to resist the thrust of the grain, the walls are of substantial construction to a height of 3 metres with corrugated sheeting used for the upper walls. This type of building can be about 100 metres by 18·5 metres with a capacity of about 1200 tonnes. Conveyors for grain distribution, fans and ducting, loading equipment and elevators tend to make this type of structure something more of a fire risk than an ordinary storage building. (For fire-fighting aspects, see the *Manual, Part 6B: Chapter 1, 'Fires in rural areas'*.—Book 14 in the new format.)

8 Automated and high-bay warehouses

Warehousing, like other industries, has developed as new techniques have been made available. For instance, the advent of the fork-lift truck changed methods of storage permitting the introduction of pallet storage and high stacking. It was only the instability of the fork-lift truck and the obstructed view of the operator, which set a limit on the height of stacks of about 8 metres.

The changing pattern of retail distribution also brought about more sophisticated supply arrangements to service the retail outlets of the large stores and supermarkets, and the progression from the fork-lift truck to tracked stacker cranes or handling machines permitted the construction of a unique type of storage building – the high-bay warehouse (Plate 32), equipped with mechanical handling facilities to varying degrees of automation. In some cases this has resulted in a totally automated handling system with computerised control, thus enabling the labour force at the warehouse and stock levels at the shops to be kept to a minimum and reducing handling costs per item stored.

Automated high-bay warehouses are constructed in two basic ways: (i) an integrated structure, where the racking constitutes the support for the roof and has attached to it the wall-cladding, which usually consists of light alloy sheets with some form of insulation to maintain desirable conditions internally. These are the bigger variety – heights of 30 metres are becoming common, and warehouses of up to 45 metres are being built in Europe; and (ii) where the racking is separate from, and does not support, the walls and roof. These tend to be smaller – between 10·6 and 12 metres in height.

Sometimes a conventional warehouse can be converted to this type of storage by the removal of all internal features not essential to the support of the walls and roof and the installation of racking and goods-handling equipment. In most cases, the result is a series of high racks (usually cellular in construction) and long narrow aisles (between 1·2 and 2·4 metres wide), with no internal dividing walls. In the United Kingdom, the floor area of these warehouses is likely to vary between 465 square metres, and 7432 square metres and their height to range from 6 to 33 metres though even greater areas and heights are distinctly possible. There are few doors and usually no windows, though in some cases 'break in' points for firemen may be provided at ground level.

Frequently, the storage and retrieval operations are remotely controlled by a push button system, or by an appropriately programmed computer. In some cases, staff travel on the cranes to pick out goods, whilst in others, conveyor belts may be used to transport goods to and from the docking points.

A diagram of the layout of a high-bay distribution centre is shown in Fig. 10.9. The goods are taken from the receiving area at Fig. 10.9(1). High user goods (i.e. goods which are most frequently demanded), arrive in loads of up to 2 tonnes and are transferred on to steel pallets or loading boards circulated horizontally on to a moving horizontal and vertical conveyor (known as a carousel conveyor) after routing information has been fed into a computer. Elevators take the pallets to the top of the building (2) after which a stacker crane places them in storage. A similar process applies to low-user goods, which are stored on adjacent racks (3). In a reverse process, an operator on the picking area (4) can select from 1200 items by computer – the goods being retrieved from storage by the stacking crane and transferred on to carousels, and thence by conveyor belts to the marshalling area (Fig. 10.10).

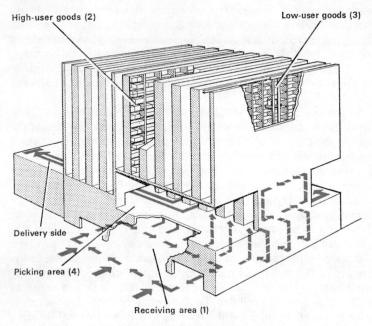

Fig. 10.9 The main rack area of a fully automated high-bay warehouse.

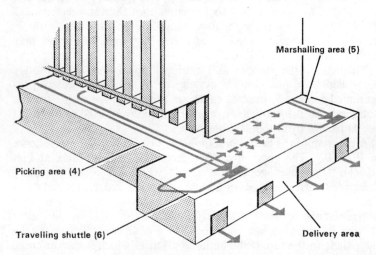

Fig. 10.10 The marshalling area shown from the opposite side of the warehouse.

High user goods come to the marshalling area (Fig. 10.10(5)) from the picking area (4) on two sides. A travelling shuttle (6) picks goods from five conveyor belts (one of which is carrying low-user goods from the lower part of the building) and directs the goods to a tilt slab conveyor which ejects them on to the appropriate loading platform. The goods are then transferred by trolleys on to the waiting lorries.

Fires in these buildings present special hazards as once inside, firemen could be faced with a fire high above ground level, approachable only through a maze of unprotected steelwork. Access may be further impeded by conveyors near the section involved and the high density storage means that a serious risk is always present. Buildings of all types may sometimes be found without adequate ventilation and with varying amounts of installed fire protection equipment, although methods are being developed to equip high-bay warehouses with automatic fire detection and extinguishing equipment. These will be designed specifically for this unusual type of building. Fire fighting in automated and high-bay warehouses will be dealt with in Book 11, 'Practical Firemanship I' (when published).

9 Hospital development

Hospital authorities have started a programme of standardisation for new premises based on a modular horizontal development in which standard hospital departments are linked together by a main common passageway at each level, together with standardised forms of vertical access, provided by lifts and stairways. The whole communication system is referred to as the 'harness communication zone' (Fig. 10.11), and the main backbone of this on each floor is known as the 'harness street'.

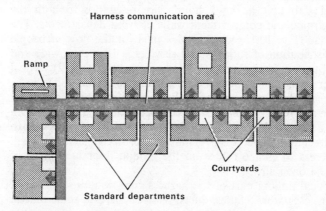

Fig. 10.11 Plan showing the 'harness communication area' linking the standard modular hospital departments.

The whole building form, which is limited to 4 floors in height, is designed within a master grid (Fig. 10.12) each square being 16.2 metres in length. Within this grid a series of modules (units) are designed, each becoming a standard department, with alternate units becoming courtyards to provide natural lighting and ventilation. The maximum depth will be 4 modules each side of a harness zone.

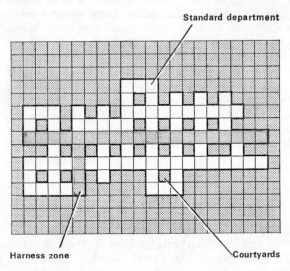

Fig. 10.12 The master grid used for designing the basic module departments linked to the 'harness street'. Each square is 16·2 metres long. The courtyards on alternate squares provide lighting and ventilation.

The structure proposed is a precast concrete 15 metres clear span frame and slab unit giving 1 hour's fire resistance to both the structural frame and compartment walls between departments. The harness zone (Fig. 10.13) which is designed for the flow of people and the distribution of supplies and services is 10 metres wide and consists of two main elements: (1) the harness street and (2) vertical linking, services, plant rooms and miscellaneous accommodation.

The harness street on each floor takes up 3 metres of the harness zone width and forms a fire-resisting compartment separating it from all other accommodation. It will be sub-divided as necessary to provide direct and safe access to a staircase (protected shaft) and will provide access to escape routes on the ground floor to a place of safety in the open air.

The vertical linking part of the harness zone contains staircases, lifts, ramps, escalators, chutes, ducts, plant rooms and some offices. All these, either individually or in a group, will form separate fire compartments apart from the harness street.

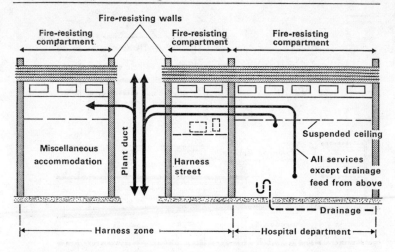

Fig. 10.13 Section showing the harness zone, which incorporates the harness street, vertical linking, services, etc.

Detailed design considerations lay great stress on fire prevention and protection measures to ensure control of fire and smoke spread, and on external facilities for adequate access for appliances.

10 Town centre development

The type of development, or redevelopment, scheme termed a 'complex', whilst not strictly within the classification of a special building, must by its very nature be examined as a complete entity. Each complex varies but, in general, the term may be taken to mean a multi-level, multi-occupancy usually of considerable extent, and it can include existing built-up areas in which some of the access roads have been rearranged, paved over, possibly roofed over, or even blocked off.

Larger complexes or developments contain cinemas, dance halls, concert halls, hotels, bowling alleys, blocks of residential flats and/or offices, as well as supermarkets, department stores, smaller shops and open-fronted market areas. These may be found set around a concourse or on each side of malls which may often be roofed over. Staircases, elevators, bridges and galleries link the various parts of the complex into a unified whole. One town centre development complex is shown in Plate 33, and Fig. 10.14 shows a diagram of a typical scheme.

Whatever layout may be adopted there should always be adequate pre-planning especially in regard to the attendance of fire appliances at key access points. With large complexes there may be a number of

161

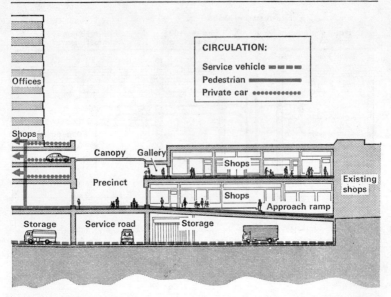

Fig. 10.14 Diagram showing a typical town centre redevelopment complex.

different blocks incorporated in the scheme and a number of entrances. Arrangements should ensure that attendance is made at the correct point according to the location of the fire, especially as the inhabitants or users of such complexes often get into the habit of referring to the address locally under one general title.

In order to assist fire brigade officers who may be concerned with the planning stages of town centre development complexes, the Home Office has issued a booklet – *Fire Prevention Guide No. 1: 'Fire precautions in town centre redevelopment'* (HMSO). This covers such points as means of escape from fire, fire warning systems and public control, means of calling the fire brigade, first-aid fire-fighting equipment, the control of smoke and heat, the siting of fire stations, identification of address, access for fire appliances, water supplies and communications for fire service use.

If the buildings in a town centre complex were constructed to Building Regulations standards, dangers of fire spread would be minimal. In many complexes this would be so restrictive in terms of commercial usage as to nullify any advantages to be gained in comprehensive development. Provision is made, therefore, for the relaxation of particular regulations where it is reasonable to assume that this would involve no material risk, i.e. where other forms of safeguard are incorporated into the complex to achieve an equal standard of safety to that called for by regulations, such as non-combustible construction and in certain cases, complete sprinkler protection. Conversely, a more stringent constructional standard than regulations allow may be necessary in some schemes.

11 Air-supported structures

Air-supported, or, as it is sometimes called, pneumatic building construction is of comparatively recent origin and ranges from the modest camper's tent to huge exhibition structures. These are being developed for many commercial and industrial applications, such as warehousing and manufacturing processes, for the agricultural and horticultural industries and for military use for garages, radar equipment protection, mobile hospitals and workshops. They are also coming into use as enclosures for swimming pools, tennis courts and other sports which are affected by adverse weather conditions. An example of an air-supported structure is shown in Fig. 10.15.

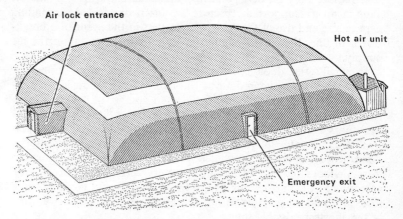

Fig. 10.15 An air-supported structure.

The most common types of pneumatic construction are:

(i) An air-inflated structure in which air is contained within ribs formed of pvc or other plastics or fabric membrane. These ribs form the 'structural elements', the columns and beams which in turn support the roof and walls.

(ii) An inflated double walled structure in which air is contained between the membranes.

(iii) An air-supported structure which consists of a single membrane supported by a small pressure above atmosphere (inflation) over the whole of the structure's internal surface.

Modifications of these systems are encountered, and sometimes combinations of more than one system. Particular designs have different characteristics from the point of view of occupant safety; for example, in the case of (iii) the designer will often incorporate lightweight steel framing for the primary purpose of providing a stable fixing for lighting equipment, but this may serve also to support the roof should the structure deflate for any reason.

Buildings of traditional construction are kept in contact with the ground by their own weight, but it will be apparent that the ballooning effect of air structures has to be resisted by 'anchoring' them firmly to the ground.

To achieve sufficient air pressure differential in an air-supported structure, low pressure fans supply air in sufficient quantity to compensate for losses through the fabric and through the doors. In order to reduce the amount of loss through the doors and to make the structure easy of access against the difference in pressure, 'air-locks' are used (Plate 34). These problems do not arise in the air-inflated types of structure as the ribs are inflated to quite a high pressure and require only an occasional top-up to keep them firm. The air fans in an air-supported structure are often duplicated, depending on the size and use of the structure, so that in the event of a breakdown in one, the standby immediately cuts in to maintain the air supply.

Ironically the door most suited to the smaller air-supported structure is the revolving door as this causes the least air loss. However as it takes so much longer for a given number of people to pass through this type of door as compared to a conventional type, revolving doors are usually considered to be unsuitable from an escape from fire point of view. If and when they are permitted, an additional door or opening must be provided, bringing more problems from air loss. Air-locks and air curtains are becoming the recognised means of access and exit, but the number of these need careful consideration to ensure that all persons within the structure can escape from fire in the shortest possible time.

The fabrics used are inherently flame-proof but most would probably melt in a fire. Any holes formed by such melting would allow the membrane to sag with possible collapse on to the fire. Many factors are involved in this aspect before conclusions can be drawn. These include the type of fabric used, the nature of jointing substance, the height and extent of the structure, and of course the size and type of fire.

The various Building Regulations are not framed to cover these types of structure and designers are, therefore, required to obtain dispensation or relaxation of the 'E' Regulations and normally the 'D' Regulations also, prior to the erection of the structure.

12 Multi-storey car parks

It was stated in Chapter 7 'Compartmentation' that in many cases the use of compartment walls and floors is mandatory in new buildings. If the compartmentation criteria were to be rigidly applied in every case the requirements in some types of building would be unnecessarily onerous. One such type is the multi-storey car park

(Fig. 10.16). In such a building of the maximum permitted size built to Building Regulation standards, all the structural elements would be required to have fire resistance of four hours and its size would be restricted so that only about 400 cars could be accommodated. The fire load is considered to be low compared with other storage buildings, the purpose group into which car-park buildings fall. Relatively few people are in the building at any one time and therefore life risk is not high. The open sides (Plate 35) would allow heat and smoke to escape rapidly so facilitating fire-fighting and the means of escape are generally good. The enforcing authorities recognise these points and also the structural problems involved in attempting compartmentation – continuous ramping, for example, is often required – and in consequence relaxation of the regulations in many of these buildings has been allowed (Plate 36).

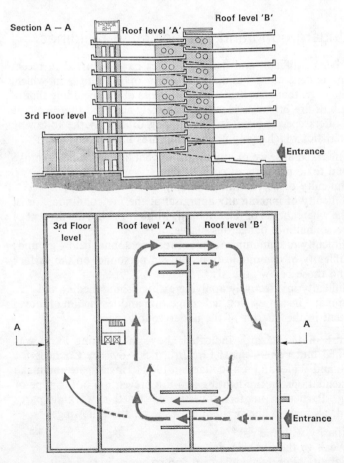

Fig. 10.16 Elevation and plan of the floor layout of a typical multi-storey car park.

As with all special buildings, the relaxations are never given as a matter of course. The authorities concerned, usually the local authority, the fire authority and the petroleum authority, will take into consideration such factors as:

(i)   materials to be used in construction;
(ii) the separation from adjoining buildings;
(iii) distances from other buildings;
(iv) access for fire appliances;
(v)   the provision of cross ventilation;
(vi) the means of escape;

when making recommendations relating to relaxation.

Different considerations apply to underground car parks, which may be multi-level, and to those in which fuelling, repair or other services are provided.

13 Underground and unfenestrated buildings

A number of difficult and dangerous fires have occurred in recent years in underground buildings or parts of buildings, in which, unfortunately, there has sometimes been loss of life including that of members of fire brigades. It will be generally accepted that this type of fire offers special hazards due, among others, to the following characteristics which many undergound fires have in common:

(i)   a marked absence of any means of ventilating the heat, smoke and toxic products of combustion;
(ii) difficulty of access and of finding one's way about;
(iii) difficulty of making any appraisal of the fire conditions, or of the whereabouts of the fire itself, without risking the descent of personnel into dangerous places;
(iv) difficulty of communication between personnel below ground;
(v)   difficulty of communication between personnel on the surface and those below ground;
(vi) difficulty in effectively applying extinguishing media; and
(vii) in many instances, unusual congestion and restriction of movement in the interior of the underground space.

Because of the hazards indicated above, a Working Party was established under the Central Fire Brigades Advisory Councils for England and Wales and for Scotland in 1967 to investigate and make recommendations on fire-fighting and fire prevention in this type of building. Particular matters investigated by this working party included, as regards the fire-fighting aspects, the following:

Familiarity with the risk
Early call to the fire brigade
Availability of correct equipment and resources in sufficient quantities

Ability to work in conditions of heat as well as smoke
Effect of heat on the human body
Hot and humid conditions
Hot and dry conditions
Types of breathing apparatus
Safe procedure for breathing apparatus wearers
Communications
Guide lines
Personal lines
The application of special fire-fighting measures.

As regards fire prevention, the following points were considered to be specially worthy of note:

Sources of ignition
Substances of high hazard
Housekeeping
Premises under construction
Detection
Constant attendance
Frequent patrolling
Monitoring of live, unattended equipment
Automatic fire detection
Early extinction
Automatic installations for special risks
Sprinklers
Containment
Compartmentation
Ventilating systems
Underfloor chambers and ducts
Areas of high hazard
Safety of occupants
Fire venting

Chapter 11
Services in buildings

In addition to their basic structure, many buildings contain some measure of special equipment designed to make them suitable for the uses to which they are to be put. In a large building, these services (as they are generally called) may include such items as electrical switchrooms with transformers and other plant, much electric cable and wiring running in ducts through a series of floors, gas pipes, cold and hot water pipes, lifts with their associated motor rooms and lift shafts, boiler rooms and fuel stores, ventilation and dust extraction plant, conveyors, machinery drives, etc.

These are of interest to the fireman in two ways. First, they may themselves be the cause of outbreaks of fire as with short circuits in defective electrical wiring, leaks from gas pipes and the ignition under certain circumstances of adjacent timberwork by steam pipes or high pressure hot-water pipes. Secondly, the ducts or wells in which they run may provide a channel for the spread of fire. Examples of this are lift wells, systems of mechanical ventilation and the holes in floors for shafting and belting which sometimes run from roof to basement in old factories.

The construction of lifts is dealt with in the *Manual, Part 6A: Chapter 36, Section II* (Book 12 in the new format). Electricity and gas are also dealt with in separate chapters in the *Manual, Part 6B* (Books 16 and 17 respectively in the new format), so that the subjects that remain to be treated here are natural and mechanical ventilation (but not fire venting systems, which are described in the Manual, Book 9), dust and solvent extraction, conveyors, machinery drives and heating installations.

1 Natural and mechanical ventilation

Ventilation in buildings may be natural or mechanical.

a. Natural ventilation

In natural ventilation the circulation and renewal of the air inside the building is effected by a combination of wind entering from outside the building and air currents generated inside. Wind enters on the windward side through doors, windows and ventilators and is drawn out by the suction on the leeward side, and up chimneys even though there be no fire. Natural ventilation is greatly increased by the internal air currents set up by fires, radiators, etc. and the natural warmth of the occupants. The warmed air rises and escapes through the tops of windows and high level ventilators, and cold air is drawn in to replace it through the doors and the bottom of windows.

Many different types of air inlet and outlet have been used at different periods and in different kinds of building. They are all, in essence, simply holes in the outer wall or roof fitted with flaps, grilles or louvres to allow air to enter or escape, at the same time excluding rain and draughts. The type most commonly used today is known as an 'air brick' and is placed at high level as an outlet in rooms which have no chimney flue. It consists usually of a 230 mm square opening in the wall protected on the outside and inside by grilles. Similarly air bricks are provided to ventilate the underside of a wooden ground floor, the air entering on the windward side, circulating under the house and out on the other side.

Low level air inlets are uncommon today but many old buildings have them, often screened by a metal tube which deflects the air upwards (Fig. 11.1). The bottom of this tube often gets filled with scraps of paper which block the inlet and may be set alight by a carelessly thrown cigarette end. In many modern buildings, particularly offices and hotels, fresh air inlets are often provided behind radiators placed under windows.

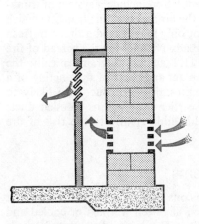

Fig. 11.1 Diagram showing the arrangement of a low level inlet.

Single-storey factories and large halls are often ventilated by means of lantern lights in a flat roof or louvred ventilators placed at the apex of a pitched roof. These provide a permanent outlet for hot air and may be very useful in a fire for this reason, but they may also tend to carry a fire into the roof space. The extract effect in a fire of such ventilators may be so great that timber in or near the ventilator may become ignited by the hot gases even though the fire is some distance away and there is no actual flame at the ventilator.

b. Mechanical ventilation

In mechanical ventilation the circulation of air is assisted or even carried out entirely by a system of fans and ducting; it is provided in very large buildings such as warehouses, where the window area is small in relation to the total volume of air; in buildings, such as cinemas, theatres, offices, etc. where large numbers of people congregate in a relatively small space and in establishments such as factories where the operatives must be protected from harmful gases and dust produced in manufacturing processes.

Mechanical ventilation may be divided into three principal groups: ventilation in which the vitiated air is extracted from the building by fans, fresh air finding its way through doors and windows: ventilation in which fresh air is forced into the building by fans, vitiated air finding its way out through doors and windows: ventilation in which fans are used both to force fresh air into the building and drive out vitiated air.

In the last two methods the air pressure inside the building is kept slightly above that outside so as to avoid incoming draughts. For this reason a balanced ventilation system is also sometimes referred to as a *plenum* (Latin: full) system, although the term is properly applied only to the second method listed above.

Most systems of mechanical ventilation include a system of trunking for distributing or extracting the air and it is this trunking which is important to the fireman as not only may it feed a fire with fresh air, but, in addition, it forms a ready channel for the spread of fire throughout the building. Fig. 11.2 shows diagrammatically the arrangement of the conditioning plant and parts of the ducting of a 'plenum' system in a large premises. Modern ducts are likely to be made of steel sheet, but in earlier installations wooden ducts were common and, of course, this adds greatly to the risk of fire spread.

2 Air conditioning systems

These systems are in effect extensions of ventilating systems in that they provide ventilation air which has been warmed or cooled and has the desired level of humidity. The basic elements of an air conditioning system are:

(i) fans for moving the air;

(ii) filters for air cleansing;

(iii) refrigerating plant connected to heat exchange surface, such as finned coils or chilled water sprays;

(iv) means for warming the air;

(v) means for humidification; and

(vi) a control system to regulate the amount of heating or cooling automatically.

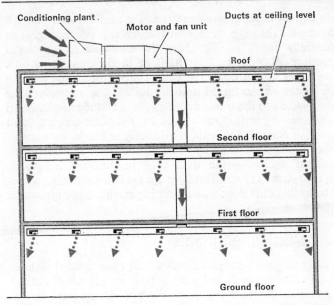

Conditioning plant. Motor and fan unit Ducts at ceiling level

Roof

Second floor

First floor

Ground floor

Fig. 11.2 Diagram showing the arrangement of a 'plenum' system for an industrial premises.

Many types of systems are available. The one chosen for a particular building depends largely upon the use of the building; for example, in a large theatre a central plant system is used in which all the air conditioning units are installed in a single plant room and serve the whole of the theatre through ducting. In a multi-storey building a zoned system is often used in which each floor (or zone) is provided with its own recirculating fan, heat booster and cooler, and each of these units are supplied with fresh air conditioned to an average temperature and humidity requirement by a 'master' unit.

Self-contained air conditioning units are also available which vary in size from quite small domestic units to a size suitable for industrial application. The larger sizes are often connected to ducting from the fresh air inlet to the distribution side for circulating the conditioned air.

3 Dust extraction

In factories where quantities of dust or fumes are produced by the processes being carried on, it is now usual to provide extract ducts for each machine (Plate 37). Where, as is very often the case, the dust or fumes are themselves flammable, the ducting and the collecting chamber may be a frequent site of fire. Various methods of protection have been tried, including generous use of sprinklers, but any such system must inevitably remain a source of danger.

171

Fires in extract ducts generally start at the machine end through overheating of a bearing or a spark from the processing. The fire is generally drawn rapidly along the duct and may cause a dust explosion either in the duct itself or in the cyclone or dust separation plant at the discharge end. The object in fire-fighting should be to cut off the forced draught quickly and so prevent the fire from spreading to the whole ducting system and the accumulated dust at the receiving end. Ducts should be, but often are not, fitted with inspection doors at intervals, particularly at bends. Opening of these doors allows a jet or spray to be directed into the interior.

Methods of collecting the dust vary in different industries. Hoppers, dust chambers and dust bags are the commonest. Cyclones used for collecting dust from wood-working machines are illustrated in Plate 38.

4 Solvent extraction plants

In almost all processes where a solvent is used there is fitted plant to draw off the solvent vapour and recover from it as much of the solvent as possible. Whether the solvent vapour-air mixture is rich enough to be within the explosive limits depends upon the process concerned and the type of vapour used, but in most cases the mixture is too weak to be explosive. The ducts lead to a recovery plant where the solvent is extracted by means of charcoal and steam; the plant is in most cases isolated from the ducting by a water trap, though this precaution is not always found.

5 Mechanical conveyors and chutes

A great variety of automatic methods of transporting materials will be found in many factories and warehouses. Their interest to the fireman lies in the fact that they are often both themselves a common source of fire and also a route by which fire can spread. There are three main systems:

a. Conveyor belts

Horizontal conveyor belts are used mainly in factories, but will also be found in grain, oil seed and other warehouses. There is always a danger of fire starting through a hot bearing in the rollers on which the belting runs and, as the belting is often itself combustible and has flammable dust or fluff adhering to it, there is a danger that a small fire will be spread rapidly to all parts of the factory to which the belting runs. If the material conveyed by the belt is combustible, there is also the danger that fire may be carried on the conveyor from an affected to an unaffected compartment. Where conveyor belting runs through a fire division wall, the opening is often protected by sprinkler heads. If there is any danger of fire being carried by a belt it is always wise to stop the system.

b. Gravity feeds

Gravity feeds will be found either in the form of pipes or of channel slides like the helter-skelter of the fairground. Both forms are used in factories and sometimes in warehouses. This method is the commonest way of conveying industrial liquids from one part of a factory to another, the liquids being pumped firstly up to large tanks on the top floor. Acids and alkalis used for industrial processes, and vegetable oils for soap manufacture are stored in this way and in a fire there is the danger that if a pipe fractures, a stream of flammable liquid will be released to feed the flames. Further, there is the added risk that if the steel tank supports are not fully protected against fire, collapse may result in the tank crashing through the whole height of the building.

The slides or chutes are often constructed of timber either because they were built before metal chutes were available or because, under certain atmospheric conditions, metal is subject to condensation which would be harmful to the process, as in flour mills. In most types of chute, inspection holes are provided and, in many cases, also cut-offs or valves which can be useful to some extent in forming a fire break.

c. Suction pipes

A third method of conveying certain materials is by the use of suction piping and is largely confined to grain and oil seed warehouses or silos. The material is sucked out of the barge or ship's hold to the top of the grain warehouse where it is carried by mechanical conveyor and finally dropped through chutes to the floors below. Further reference to conveyor systems in particular industries will be found in the *Manual, Part 6C* (Books 14 and 15 in the new format).

6 Machinery drives

In modern factories it is usual to arrange for each machine to be driven by its own individual electric motor (or sometimes a series of motors). Before the development of electric drives, however, machinery was usually driven from a central source of power such as a large steam engine through line shafting and belting. In some cases this equipment has been partially modernised by the substitution of a large gas or oil engine or an electric motor. In a multi-floor factory this method of driving, which is still quite common, presents considerable fire hazards because the engine is located on the ground floor and the drive taken by means of belts to the line shafting on each of the floors above. These belts often pass through holes cut in the floors which thus form a vertical flue through the building, up which fire can spread with great rapidity.

The line shafting runs through the factory and carries at intervals pulleys from which belts take the drive to the individual machines.

The shafting is carried in numerous brackets suspended from the underside of the ceilings and the bearings are often heavily encrusted with congealed oil and grease, as also is the surrounding woodwork converting the whole into a serious fire hazard. The presence of overhead line shafting and belting leads to congestion on the floors of the factory, especially in textile mills, and to small spaces between machines. It may be found that the works manager of a factory may be disinclined to stop all the machinery in a mill for the sake of a fire in one shop, but the risk of being caught in running belting while moving about in smoke is very great and, if conditions appear unsafe, the fire brigade officer should insist upon having the machinery stopped before any of his men enter the shop where the fire is.

In some of the oldest buildings, such as cotton and lace mills, the drive may be by means of an internal vertical shaft which drives the line shafting at each floor through bevel gearing. In this case there is an unenclosed opening which runs throughout the height of the building and which can easily assist fire spread. Alternatively, and especially in Scotland, the drive may be by shafting beneath the floor, carried in conduits with iron lids, each machine being driven by a belt passing through holes in the floorboards. This type of drive relieves congestion in the shop and there is less danger of a man becoming caught up in the drive. It does, however, offer great opportunities for quick fire spread, since the accumulation of fluff and oil in the channels may transmit fire throughout the shop, where it is likely to appear through the belt holes and so involve the floorboards and any fluff round the machines. It should be unnecessary to emphasise the dangers of fire spread inherent in this type of drive.

7 Heating systems

a. Classification

The number of heating systems available is almost unlimited as to combinations of the various components, such as the fuel, method used for heat distribution and the type of heater can be effected in so many ways. For all practical purposes, systems can be divided into two groups:

(i) direct systems, in which the fuel (or energy) is consumed in the room to be heated; and

(ii) indirect systems, in which energy is transferred from some central point outside the space to be heated, to equipment within that space.

The direct systems are further subdivided according to whether the fuel (or energy source) is solid: coal, coke, etc. – liquid: oil – gas: town and natural gas, liquified petroleum gas – or electrical. A further subdivision is made according to the form of the heat emitted. For example, a portable paraffin heater is classified as a direct system using oil as its fuel and the heat emission is either convected or radiant depending upon the design of the appliance.

The indirect systems are subdivided according to the type of 'transmitting medium' which may be liquid, vapour or gas, and these systems are also further subdivided according to their heat-emitting element. A low pressure hot water system, for example, is classified as an indirect system using any of the fuels mentioned, but the 'transmitting medium' is liquid (hot water), the heat being emitted from a series of pipes and radiators. It should be noted that in the indirect group the fuels can be interchanged in any combination of the transmitting medium and heat emitter. This is not so in direct systems as the fuel directly relates to the emitter with no intermediate stage.

b. Direct systems

The majority of these systems are so commonplace that reference will be made only to those systems which are of particular interest to the fireman from a legislative or fire protection point of view. This group comprises open fires, stoves, gas and electric radiant and convector heaters and block storage heaters. In some cases, fan units are incorporated and in others ducting is used to direct the heated air to the various spaces.

(1) Open fires

The *Building Regulations 1972* (England and Wales) require that an anchorage for an effective fireguard shall be provided for solid fuel fires designed to burn directly on a hearth.

(2) Paraffin heaters

Portable paraffin heating appliances offered for sale either new or secondhand, must conform to the *Oil Heaters Regulations 1962 and 1966* made under the *Consumer Protection Act 1961*.

c. Indirect systems (central heating)

In central heating installations energy from fuel is converted to heat and then distributed around the building to heat emitters, such as radiators by pipes and ducts. The most common type of system is that which employs low pressure hot water, but other heat transfer media are used in systems which could freeze, including various oils. The system consists basically of a boiler, furnace or other heat producing mechanism, pipes or ducts to carry the water (or other heating medium) and later return it, and also heat emitters in the various parts of the building. The hazards associated with boilers and fuel storage are given in the *Manual, Part 6C: Section 5* (Book 17 in the new format).

175

d. Block storage heaters

Block storage heaters enable heat produced electrically to be stored during off-peak hours for warming rooms during the rest of the day. They are more often referred to as night storage heaters, and consist of resistance elements enclosed in ceramic or concrete material contained in a partially insulated steel casing. Loadings vary between 1·5 and 3·5 kW. The maximum temperature on the surface is about 85°C which declines to about 40°C at the end of the day. The fireclay storage materials reach a temperature of about 200°C. It is important that the outlets from the individual heaters are kept free of obstruction.

Developments of this type of heating are storage fan heaters and electric storage warm air systems. In both these the control of rate of heat release is designed to be more precise than the system described above and ducting is often incorporated, thus extending the use of such systems to central heating.

e. Domestic warm air heating systems

Air heating units are usually of the recirculating type. The air is drawn from one or more points and after being warmed in a heat exchanger, the energy source of which can be oil, gas or electricity, is distributed by a system of ducts and grilles to the spaces to be warmed. The supply, return and transfer grilles may be located in the ceiling, walls or in the floor. The grilles, therefore, create a means by which smoke and hot gases may be spread from one room to another. The heating units are not in themselves a particular hazard.

The recirculation of the warmed air is carried out by means of a fan and ducting which are often supplemented by transfer grilles. These latter simply allow the warmed air to pass from one space to an adjacent one. The fan is thermostatically controlled and stops when the temperature of a room (or controlled area) reaches a predetermined level. It follows therefore that this would happen should a fire occur external to the system. Nevertheless, smoke from the fire still has a path via the ducting and grilles to other parts of the building.

Perforations of fire-resisting partitions by this type of unit heating system are kept to an absolute minimum compatible with the efficient working of the system to guard against this potential smoke fire-spread hazard.

Both electric and gas warm air domestic types of heating can therefore be classified as both 'direct' and 'indirect' depending upon whether the heat is transferred from a central point by ducting (indirect) or whether heat is immediately convected from the storage heater to the space to be heated (direct).

Chapter 12
Access for fire appliances to buildings

When a fire occurs in a building it is essential that fire appliances can readily approach the building as quickly as possible. The size of a building will also be taken into account when deciding upon the first attendance, i.e. whether a turntable ladder will be included with other first-line pumping appliances. Since different types of appliance require different access conditions, it is by the volume and height of the building that the access requirements are determined.

The Building Regulations in England and Wales do not contain measures for the assistance of the fire service, such as access for fire-fighting, because the powers in the originating Act (the *Public Health Act of 1961*) did not extend to such purposes. New powers will be available from the passage of the *Health and Safety at Work etc. Act 1974,* and this will doubtless increase the scope of Building Regulations accordingly. The *Building Standards (Scotland) (Consolidation) Regulations* and the *London Building Acts,* however, do cover this aspect of protection for certain types of occupancy. The Home Office Fire Department has issued guidance on access for fire appliances (*Fire Prevention Note No. 1/70*), and it is this guidance which is often used in the planning stage of building projects. The following notes and diagrams are based on this Fire Prevention Note.

1 Buildings not fitted with rising mains*

a. Buildings not exceeding 7000 cubic metres

(1) Floors not higher than 6 metres

One or two storey buildings of less than 7000 cubic metres with no floor higher than 6 metres require access roads (the dimensions of which are given in Table 5 on page 180) to enable pumping appliances to approach within 46 metres of any point within the area of the ground floor.

In the case of single-family dwelling-houses, however, this requirement is waived provided that they have access roads which permit fire appliances to approach within 46 metres of the front or the back door, whichever is the nearer approach for wheeled vehicles.

---

* Therefore relying totally on hose and equipment carried on the appliances.

(2) Floors between 6 and 9 metres in height

With the number of storeys not stated, access roads (see Table 5) are required to permit pumping appliances to approach to within 30 metres of any point within the area of the ground floor of the building.

(3) Floors higher than 9 metres

Access roads for turntable ladders and/or hydraulic platforms (see Table 5) are required along one or more of the perimeter walls and should have a total length of at least one-sixth of the combined length of all the perimeter walls. There must be access to the interior of the building from such access roads.

b. Building between 7000 and 28 400 cubic metres

(1) Floors not higher than 9 metres

Access roads, which must be able to take pumping appliances, are required along one or more walls in which there are means of entry to the interior of the building, the length of the access road being not less than one-sixth of the total length of the perimeter walls (Fig. 12.1(1)).

(2) Floors higher than 9 metres

Access roads for turntable ladders and/or hydraulic platforms are required along two perimeter walls (Fig. 12.1(2)).

c. Buildings between 28 400 and 56 800 cubic metres

Access roads are required along two perimeter walls for pumping appliances (for floors not higher than 9 metres) or for all appliances (for floors above 9 metres in height) (Fig. 12.1(2)).

d. Buildings between 56 800 and 85 200 cubic metres

Access roads as for (c) above are required along three perimeter walls (Fig. 12.1(3)).

e. Buildings over 85 000 cubic metres

Access roads as for (c) above are required along all sides of the building (an island site) (Fig. 12.1(4)).

2 Flats and maisonettes not fitted with rising mains

Where such buildings, whatever their volume, have all floors below 9 metres above ground level, access roads are required so that fire appliances may approach within 46 metres of any point within any maisonettes. For flats and maisonettes over 9 metres in height access roads are required for all types of appliance (as 1(c) above).

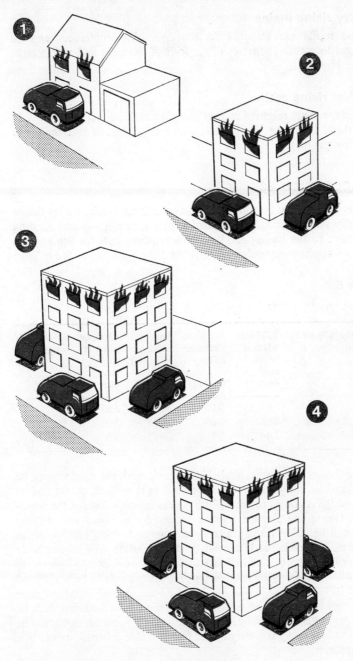

Fig. 12.1 Diagram showing the recommended access for fire appliances to buildings. For explanation of the various categories, see text.

3 All buildings fitted with rising mains

a. Dry rising mains

Access roads are required so that pumping appliances can be brought to within 18 metres of the foot of the main and within sight of the building.

b. Wet rising mains

Access roads are required so that pumping appliances can be brought to within 18 metres of the ground floor access point of each main and within sight of the building.

4 Access routes

Access routes may be public highways, private roads, footpaths or specially strengthened and defined routes through the surrounding landscape to the building. The access requirements for the various types of appliance are shown in Table 5.

Table 5

Access requirements for appliances

Type of appliance	Minimum width of access road (metre)	Minimum clearance height (metre)	Turning circle (diameter) (metre)	Minimum width of gateways etc. (metre)	Laden weight (tonne)
Pumping	3·66	3·66	16·76	3·05	10
Turntable ladder	3·66	3·66	18·90	3·05	12
Hydraulic platform	3·66	3·96	20·12	3·05	18 (max.)

Where the use of a turntable ladder is envisaged, the road should be positioned so that its nearer edge is not less than 4·88 metres and its further edge is not more than 10·06 metres from the face of the building. A turntable ladder standing on a road positioned within these limits will be able to operate to its maximum height. The hydraulic platform, however, needs a road or hardstanding 4·88 metres wide because of the spread of its jacks and, if it is required to operate to its maximum height, the road or hardstanding needs to be positioned so that its nearer edge is not less than 1.83 metres and its farther edge is not more than 7.32 metres from the face of the building. Roads, including any manhole covers and public utility service pits, should be capable of carrying the weights set out in Table 5 for the respective appliances.

Manual of Firemanship:
Revised Structure

Book 1 Elements of combustion and extinction

Part	Part	Chapter	First published
1 Physics of combustion	1	1	1943
2 Chemistry of combustion	1	1	1943
3 Methods of extinguishing fire	1	2 and	1945
	6A	32(III)	1945

Book 2 Fire brigade equipment

Part	Part	Chapter	First published
1 Hose	1	4	1943
2 Hose fittings	1	5	1943
3 Ropes and lines, knots, slings, etc.	1	7 and	1943
	6A	39	1945
4 Small gear	1	13	1943

Book 3 Fire extinguishing equipment

Part	Part	Chapter	First published
1 Hand and stirrup pumps	1	8	1943
2 Portable chemical extinguishers	1	9	1943
3 Foam and foam-making equipment	1	10	1943

Book 4 Pumps and special appliances

Part	Part	Chapter	First published
1 Pumping appliances	2	1	1944
2 Practical pump operation	2	2	1944
3 Special appliances	2	6	1944

Book 5 Fire brigade ladders

Part	Part	Chapter	First published
1 Extension ladders	1	6	1943
2 Escapes and escape mountings	2	3	1944
3 Turntable ladders	2	4	1944
4 Hydraulic platforms	2	5	1944

Book 6 Breathing apparatus and resuscitation

Part	Part	Chapter	First published
1 Breathing apparatus	1	11	1943
2 Operational procedure	6A	32(V)	1945
3 Resuscitation	1	12	1943

Book 7 Hydraulics and water supplies

Part		Part	Chapter	First published
1	Hydraulics	3	19	1943
2	Hydrants and water supplies	3	20	1943
3	Water relaying	3	21	1943
	Appendices	3		1943

Book 8 Building construction and structural fire protection

Part		Part	Chapter	First published
1	Materials	4	23	1949
2	Elements of structure	4	23	1949
3	Building design	4	23	1949

Book 9 Fire protection of buildings

Part		Part	Chapter	First published
1	Fire extinguishing systems	4	24/26	1949
2	Fire alarm systems	5	28	1955
3	Fire venting systems	4	23	1949

Book 10 Fire brigade communications

Part		Part	Chapter	First published
1	The public telephone system and its relationship to the fire service	5	27	1955
2	Mobilising arrangements	5	29	1955
3	Call-out and remote control systems	5	30	1955
4	Radio	5	31	1955
5	Automatic fire alarm signalling systems	5	28	1955

Book 11 Practical Firemanship I

Part		Part	Chapter	First published
1	Practical fire fighting	6A	32	1945
2	Methods of entry into buildings	6A	35	1945
3	Control at a fire	6A	33	1945

Book 12 Practical Firemanship II

Part		Part	Chapter	First published
1	Method of rescue	6A	36	1945
2	Ventilation at fires	6A	37	1945
3	Salvage	6A	38	1945
4	After a fire	6A	34	1945

Book 13 Fireboats and ship fires

Part		Part	Chapter	First published
1	Fireboats and their equipment	7	1	1944
2	Seamanship	7	2	1944
3	Firemanship	7	2	1944
4	Fire in ships	7	3	1944

NOTES

NOTES

NOTES

Printed in England for Her Majesty's Stationery Office by Staples Printers Limited at
The Priory Press, St Albans, Hertfordshire.

Dd 506835   K200   11/75